PRAISE FOR THE BOOK

Profoundly touching and unsettling. Through the experiences of veterinary students, Nadine Dolby offers deep insights into our society's problematic relations with animals. She shows that what goes on in veterinary education is not solely an intra-disciplinary matter; it is an urgent concern for society at large. We need to radically change the situation of animals in society, and this change must begin in the education system. We should read Nadine Dolby's eye-opening account as a bold and compassionate guide in this necessary transformation process.

—**Helena Pedersen**, Senior Lecturer, Unit for General Didactics and Pedagogic Work, University of Gothenburg, Sweden; author of *Schizoanalysis and Animal Science Education and Animals in Schools: Processes and Strategies in Human-Animal Education*

In *Learning Animals*, Nadine Dolby provides a critical, richly descriptive point of departure for much-needed conversations about learning with, rather than on and about, our more-than-human world. It will come as no surprise that Dolby's research is the product of a well-practiced and remarkably sensitive qualitative eye. Qualitative researchers, in particular, will value the deeply reflective methodological chapter that details the experienced researcher's continued growth through deliberate, close attention to human and non-human relationships.

—**Amy Stich**, Associate Professor of Higher Education, University of Georgia, USA

Learning Animals offers a unique educational perspective into the pedagogy of veterinary training. As a professor of education, Nadine Dolby adds a necessary voice to the conversation about animals in our society: how we learn about them, how we think about them, how we treat them, and how it is all connected. Much of what is written about veterinary education is produced by veterinarians themselves. But if we want to know the impact of educational practices more fully, then we need to read the analyses of scholars of education, social scientists, those in the humanities, and all others outside of the profession who study these institutions. Dolby conducted in-depth interviews with a cohort of veterinary students over the four-year course of their program. In this book, she helps guide the reader through stories spanning four years of explicit and implicit instruction on how students are to think and feel about animals, supporting her research with detailed excerpts from intensive conversations with students. Her work aptly presents her findings with rich data, so the reader can understand this social scene and its consequences; but she also brings an empathetic compassion to this presentation, so the reader can understand why they should care.

—**Jenny Vermilya**, author of *Identity, Gender, and Tracking: The Realty of Boundaries for Veterinary Students*

In *Learning Animals*, Nadine Dolby examines how veterinary education shapes the ways veterinary students experience animals and construct professional identities. Based on in-depth personal narratives of veterinary students collected over five years, Dolby shows how veterinary education transforms the relationships students have with animals. Consequently, even those perceived as experts on animal welfare and rights have little knowledge and understanding in these areas. Through meticulous research and masterly writing, *Learning Animals* shines valuable light on the philosophical and ethical assumptions behind the formal veterinary curriculum. Dolby's book opens up new possibilities for understanding and re-imagining relationships between humans and other animals.

—**Leslie Irvine**, Professor and Undergraduate Chair,
Department of Sociology, University of Colorado Boulder, USA

Nadine Dolby has constructed *Learning Animals* to provide the first, critical qualitative study of the perspectives and experiences of those who are often considered society's experts on nonhuman animals as they study to become veterinarians. This qualitative research study demonstrates the moral tensions imposed when the love of other living beings is countered by society's privileging of human needs and desires over all others. While learning to address the suffering of nonhuman animals, veterinarians are taught to inflict harm on them resulting in both narrowed human/nonhuman relations and increased mental (and physical) anguish for both nonhuman and human animals. Increasingly, human/nonhuman relations are recognized as important in a range of fields, from anthropology, sociology, education, and critical animal studies, to reconceptualizations of qualitative research in ways that acknowledge the multispecies entanglements and anthropocentrism often present in even justice oriented qualitative research. What these relations mean for living with other creatures is not often acknowledged or examined. This volume describes an extremely important and timely project that challenges dominant knowledge in a field that has attempted to claim expertise regarding nonhuman creatures. Further, the insights are broadly applicable to our understanding of the problems imposed by human animals on other animals as well as other forms of life and materiality. *Learning Animals* provides a critical perspective for everyone concerned with justice for those who have historically suffered as objects of human privilege - concerns that are of profound and long-term consequence for all of us, demonstrating the need to radically rethink what we think we know and how we relate to all living others around us.

—**Gaile S. Cannella**, Former Professor Texas A&M University,
Arizona State University; and Velma Schmidt Endowed Chair of
Critical Childhood Studies, the University of North Texas, USA

What does the process of becoming a veterinary professional do to our souls, and what does that show us about how our society regards animals (and those who work with them)? Nadine Dolby explores these questions through a longitudinal study of veterinary students in North America, but the issues she raises speak to many of the problems that trouble the modern veterinary sector across the developed world. She argues that the gruelling process of veterinary training forces students to adopt a mindset where, paradoxically, their original love for animals is devalued and driven underground. Is professionalism a matter of acquiring technical skills and knowledge, or of forcing conformity with a worldview where animals are valued conditionally and welfare is too often compromised?

This thought-provoking book is a welcome contribution to the new field of veterinary humanities, bringing analysis from sociology and other disciplines to bear on the problematic subject of veterinary education and work today. Dolby clearly reveals the ethical difficulties of this challenging sector. For those becoming, living as, educating or supporting veterinarians, her perceptive insights offer a troubling but illuminating basis for deep reflection on the modern difficulties of professional identity.

—**Alison Skipper**, MRCVS, Department of History, King's College London, and Co-Convenor, Veterinary Humanities UK

As this excellent book demonstrates, one way to understand a profession is to determine how people in the field are educated. I have been involved with veterinary education since the early 1970s, at which time the role model was the "macho tough guy" who was famous for "punching out" a recalcitrant bull. I took offense at that approach, and helped to erode that mind set. As greater and increasing numbers of veterinary students were from an urban background, sensitivity to the animals became increasingly common. Simultaneously, small animal and companion animal concerns increased significantly, inevitably changing veterinary school teaching. The author is an early student of these changes, which greatly influenced her teaching and scholarship. I would go so far as to suggest that her work constitutes an invaluable path to understanding recent changes in veterinary education and practice.

—**Bernard E. Rollin**, Professor of Philosophy, Animal Sciences, and Biomedical Sciences, Colorado State University, USA

Learning Animals
Curriculum, Pedagogy and Becoming a Veterinarian

Nadine Dolby

CRC Press
Taylor & Francis Group
Boca Raton London New York

CRC Press is an imprint of the
Taylor & Francis Group, an **informa** business

First edition published 2022
by CRC Press
6000 Broken Sound Parkway NW, Suite 300, Boca Raton, FL 33487-2742

and by CRC Press
2 Park Square, Milton Park, Abingdon, Oxon, OX14 4RN

CRC Press is an imprint of Taylor & Francis Group, LLC

ISBN: 978-1-032-21781-9 (hbk)
ISBN: 978-1-032-21259-3 (pbk)
ISBN: 978-1-003-26998-4 (ebk)

DOI: 10.1201/9781003269984

Typeset in Times LT Std
by Apex CoVantage, LLC

Contents

Foreword ix
Acknowledgments.. xiii
Author xvii

Chapter 1 Introduction: Animals, Education, and Change..................................... 1

Chapter 2 Animals in Education: An Overview... 13

Chapter 3 Beginnings: Contexts, Memories, and Stories 25

Chapter 4 Encountering Animal Bodies... 39

Chapter 5 Stepping Out: Learning in the Wild.. 59

Chapter 6 Endings: There Are No Animals Here.. 79

Chapter 7 Telling New Stories: Toward Different Animal and
Human Futures... 99

Chapter 8 Turning Stories into New Love: Possibilities 115

Chapter 9 A Researcher's Tale: Making Change for Animals 125

Coda... 139
References... 141
Index 155

Foreword

When my daughter was a junior in high school, she told me something that made my blood run cold. No, she hadn't been caught with drugs in her locker. She hadn't been arrested for shoplifting. She wasn't dropping out of school to become a Phish Head. No, she told me she wanted to become a veterinarian. "Oh god," I thought to myself. "Please. Not that." This may seem a strange reaction. Who wouldn't want their child to pursue a career that is socially valuable and respected, intellectually challenging, maybe even (if you can avoid the staggering weight of student loans) financially viable? My worry centered on the fact that my daughter has a tender heart and seems to have sprung from the womb an ardent lover of animals. And if you love animals, becoming a veterinarian may, in the idiom of my daughter's generation, just crush your soul.

During her last year of high school and first two years of college, my daughter began the process of making veterinary school a reality. The steps to becoming a competitive candidate are grueling. On top of having a 4.0 GPA and taking a stiff load of course prerequisites—molecular biology, organic chemistry, and genetics— you also need experience working with animals in some capacity. Other applicants, she told me, would have an average of about 1000 hours as vet techs, volunteers in shelters, members of 4-H, or employees on farms. So, my daughter signed up: she volunteered at a horse rescue, at two different humane societies, and at a wild-life rehabilitation center, and she shadowed veterinarians in the community several afternoons a week for two years.

As it turned out, and to my great relief, she changed course mid-way through college and is happily pursuing a graduate degree in ecology. Although she loved learning science and enjoyed her time with the dogs at the shelter and horses at the rescue, she grew more and more disenchanted with the actual day-to-day work of the veterinarians she shadowed. The people working in the veterinary clinics seemed unhappy; the animals were sometimes treated with indifference and even a casual brutality. When she asked the veterinarians with whom she had been working whether they liked what they did and would choose to do it all again and become veterinarians, they all said no. Every single one.

After reading Nadine Dolby's *Learning Animals*, I am even more convinced that my daughter's decision was a good one, that she dodged a life-sized bullet.

An educator and animal advocate, Dolby, trains her keen attention on what happens to the bright and eager go-getters who decide they want to enter the veterinary profession. She follows a cohort of veterinary students through their matriculation into veterinary school until their graduation four years later. We hear, in their own words, the stories of what inspired these young people to become veterinarians, how they cope with the arduous process of mastering a vast quantity of medical information in the classroom, and to what they experience as they finally begin clinicals.

Reading Dolby's interviews with students over the course of their training is part horror story, part tragedy, and often deeply affecting. You know how the story is going to end, even from the start. Excitement and dedication become detachment; the

soft core of empathy hardens into a shell. The animals who were at once in the foreground of students' lives—often the reason they wanted to become a veterinarian—
these very animals seem to disappear. They become absent, vague, and nondescript.
Not feeling, thinking individuals.

Students in Dolby's cohort learn veterinary medicine, yes. But they also come
away having uncritically accepted and acquiesced to the norms and values of the
profession, even when these involve the imposition of pain and suffering on the very
animals these students are being trained to heal. Dolby helps us understand what
these norms and values are and where they originated (out of economic exigencies).
And she helps us understand what is not only absent from veterinary medicine but
actually erased: a love for animals. Vet students they learn about and on, but rarely
with animals.

The experiences of these students are a microcosm of a larger story of how, as
Dolby puts it, "Society's primary teachers about animals are schooled: what they
learn and do and what is absent, hidden, or simply ignored." Dolby's research is not
only about what and how veterinary students learn, but it is also about how and what
the rest of us learn about animals through one of society's most trusted sources of
information about animals.

As Dolby notes, many of us learn about animals from our veterinarians. Not
only might we learn about the lifecycle of the mosquito who carries heartworm and
the "100 Top Dog Breeds" from the posters in the veterinary clinic waiting room.
Through watching how our vet moves around, touches, and talks to our animal,
we learn ways of interacting. We learn to attend—or not—to the inner experiences
of the animals we keep as pets. We might learn that restraint and muzzling for an
injection are fine (the dog is struggling, but like Descartes, we may be blind to the
fact that a dog's visible cries and protestations are expressions of deep feeling, in this
case of panic and fear). We absorb a narrative of what it means to be a responsible
dog owner or cat owner. We learn whether it is acceptable to surgically remove the
claws from a cat, cut away pieces of a dog's ears, or cut off a puppy's tail to create a
certain look, or remove the voice box of a dog who barks more than we want. If our
veterinarian offers these "services," we may assume that they are benign.

We learn other things, too. Vets affirm, by their presence within and facilitation
of animal agriculture, that the meat in our grocery store aisle is "humane," that
cows and pigs in confined animal feeding operations (CAFOs) are happy and healthy
because they have a veterinarian watching over them and confirming that their welfare is good, and that consuming animal flesh is normative. Vets also, by enabling
the biomedical research juggernaut, affirm that exploiting the bodies of other animals is a normal and morally acceptable practice.

We all have something to learn from Dolby's book—whether we are invested in
the veterinary profession or not. But for those who work within this field, as especially for those who teach future generations of veterinarians, the message is particularly crucial. She asks veterinary educators to reassess not only *what* but also *how*
students learn about animals—for the sake of animals and, perhaps even more, for
the sake of those students who bravely choose this path.

Veterinary educators do a great disservice to students—and, indeed, cause profound damage—by glossing over the sometimes ugly commitments of the field, by not encouraging students to ask why a pig might be treated differently from a dog and why a pet pig has her nails painted by adoring students while an "ag" pig is subjected to repeated, painful snaring practice by groups of students being initiated into the cult of large animal medicine. Why are animal bodies a necessary part of the human food supply? Is a "humane endpoint" ever really humane? Why is a chicken categorized as a "large" animal while a Great Dane is "small"? How can a professional oath require a commitment to promote animal welfare while at the same time always placing human interests first? Yes, there are many contradictions in how we think about and treat animals. Yet instead of being encouraged to explore for themselves these perplexing anomalies, veterinary students are expected to go along with the game and not question the rules.

Veterinarians are tasked with the impossible: put human needs and desires first but attend to suffering in animals. Love animals but be ready and willing to inflict harm. This Mission Impossible puts students and the professionals they are becoming at risk. Suicide rates among veterinarians are shockingly high; moral distress, anxiety, depression, and other mental health issues are rampant; many, as my daughter discovered, experience dissatisfaction with their work. A more compassionate approach to veterinary curriculum would provide veterinary students and veterinarians—and veterinary educators themselves—the tools and space, as well as the permission, to think through and speak openly about the profound moral tensions inherent in their work.

Dolby focuses a small lens on veterinary education and offers a compelling narrative of what happens to students and the animals they learn on and about. As such, *Learning Animals* is a critically important book for veterinary educators and for prospective and current students. It is also a book with much broader reach. But Dolby's book also has relevance for everyone who cares about the intertwined fates of humans and our fellow creatures. The students who Dolby discusses through this book, as they struggle with the day-to-day challenges of veterinary school, are a microcosm of a larger struggle to come to terms with our profoundly unhealthy relationship with other forms of life.

Jessica Pierce

Acknowledgments

This book would not have been possible without the veterinary students who graciously and bravely shared their stories with me through the five years of this research project. To them, I owe my first and lasting thanks. I also need to thank the Veterinary College at Central Midwest University (a pseudonym) for their permission to do this research at their institution and for their help facilitating my contact with students, with scheduling, and access to rooms for interviews. I know that they may feel many places of discomfort and disagreement in this book. I understand that and appreciate their willingness to allow an outsider into their world, and to thus open up conversations about veterinary education to scholars from other fields.

As I started to think about writing the acknowledgments for this book, I went back and re-read the acknowledgments for my two previous single author books, published in 2001 and 2012. As I did this, I remembered the human and non-human animals who have shaped my journey to this point, and the experiences that I have been privileged to have through my life. Some of these people and animals have since died, though they continue with me still every day. Connie Lagally, a longtime neighbor and friend, died from complications from multiple sclerosis in December 2020. Connie and I volunteered together at our local animal shelter, every week, from 2008 until 2020. As her multiple sclerosis progressed, she could no longer stand, and I joined her every week to help her continue to brush, comb, and comfort cats until a few months before her death. Connie and I had our differences—she was a very stubborn person. But she was also extremely dedicated and strong: she never wavered on her vision and what she saw as her contribution to the world. Greg Dimitriadis' death more than seven years ago was a turning point in my life. I know that there are many who are uncomfortable acknowledging that he died by suicide. I understand. But, like the veterinary profession, my own field of educational research needs to begin to break the silence around mental illness so we can help others who are struggling. Greg's words and voice still reverberate through my work and writing, as they have since we first met in the fall of 1995 during graduate school at the University of Illinois at Urbana-Champaign. Many of the non-human animals in my life have also passed: Rusty, Helio, Bubba, and Walter. I carry each of them with me.

Many new human and non-human animals and experiences have of course come into my life and have contributed to my ability to do this research. I extend my thanks to everyone who has helped me turn Animal Advocates of Greater Lafayette from a dream on a piece of paper to a small, but vibrant and growing, non-profit organization. I particularly need to thank Candace Putnam, who has been with me almost from the very beginning. When the COVID-19 pandemic and the shutdowns hit in the spring of 2020, we were quickly thrust into the local spotlight and into the work of pet food distribution. Over the remainder of 2020, we collected and distributed more than 40,000 pounds of pet food to our local community. Overnight (literally) we had to become experts in supply chain management, storage, and distribution. I could not have done this without Candace. Karen Hearn and Savannah Rambis have also taken on major roles in the organization, which is allowing us to grow, expand our services and programs, and to help more families and pets in our community. Any royalties from this book will be donated to this organization.

Both swimming and yoga helped me immensely as I coped with the stress of trying to write a book and run a local non-profit organization during a global pandemic. Chris Klinge at West Lafayette Junior/Senior High School directs an amazing aquatics program: she has an uncanny ability to quietly but deliberately build a welcoming environment and a feeling that you are part of a community of swimmers. It is not an exaggeration to say that most of this book was written in lane 1 of the pool. Adriene Mishler (of Yoga with Adriene fame) and Benji are also a constant presence in my life, and I owe them both my thanks.

I know it intensely weird to thank Goodwill, but I am going to do so anyway, in the hope of helping other writers who are struggling to put the pieces together. When we moved across town a couple years ago, we ended up living in a neighborhood that is about half a mile from Goodwill. I went there frequently when I was stuck in my thinking, and the pool/swimming was not available or practical. Goodwill (or any thrift store) is a fantastic place for qualitative researchers and writers, because there, you are forced to put the pieces together for yourself (in a limited, not endless, space), just as you are in research and writing. Goodwill is a jumble of items, but also a jumble of ideas. The process of finding the perfect vase, sweater, wall hanging, bowl, dishes, glasses, bag, or anything else at Goodwill requires imagination and creativity: nothing is curated for you, you must do it yourself. Doing this repeatedly as we staged our former house for sale and set up and organized our new home over the past two years has made me a sharper thinker and writer.

Now on to more traditional thanks—Purdue University's five-year Faculty Scholar Award provided both financial support and inspiration for this project. It makes a difference to receive a multi-year award, as it helps psychologically to realize it is okay to commit to a long-term, longitudinal project. A sabbatical in the spring of 2021 allowed me to write this book. COVID presented some challenges, as I was unable to complete planned travel, but the circumstances also forced me (and the rest of the world) to stay home, and thus to write. I was extremely nervous about working with a new editor at Taylor & Francis after so many years of collaboration and friendship with Catherine Bernard, but Alice Oven has been incredibly helpful, responsive, and supportive. I feel that in many ways, Alice is a fellow traveler, and I am very happy for my first publication with CRC Press. I have been an admirer of Jessica Pierce's work for many years, and it took some courage for me to ask her to write the foreword. I am thrilled that she agreed. Her foreword is a brilliant essay in and of itself—that her writing serves as the foreword to my book is a great privilege. I of course thank the reviewers of the book proposal and the manuscript for their thoughts and helpful advice as I mapped out the framework for the book. I thank Amy Stich for her continuing support and wise counsel.

I have many human and non-human animals to thank in my multi-species family. My daughter Natalie is now 14 and has started her first year of high school. She continues to both delight and frustrate me, as teenagers will. She is well on her way to becoming a strong, independent person who will contribute to the world and to others' well-being. I am of course thrilled that she is an avid reader and loves to write (and swim!). Orie, my long-time feline companion, is still with me. He is of course older, but his slightly ornery and simultaneously protective and nurturing personality has not changed, and it suits me. We remain the best of friends. Pizzazz and Gus prefer my husband, Stephen, but I continue to love them. Our newest feline addition, Otis, has recently taken residence in our garage. We are working on building trust with him and integrating him into our family. Eddie, my new best friend and side-kick, was not a planned pandemic puppy, but we adopted him from a local rescue in February 2020, and thus he de facto became one (though not the puppy part . . .). Eddie has multiple health problems, and almost died several times in the spring of 2020 as the world was shutting down. I need to thank Tippecanoe Animal Hospital for keeping him alive in a moment of incredible global uncertainty. Despite the chaos unfolding everywhere, they never forgot that Eddie and I needed them.

Finally, once again, I need to thank my husband, Stephen. Despite our ups and downs, we are still together and moving forward into a shared future.

Author

Nadine Dolby is Professor of Curriculum Studies at Purdue University, West Lafayette, Indiana, USA. She is the author or editor of seven books and has published widely in the field of animals, society, and education. She has conducted research, lived, and worked in South Africa, Australia, and the United States. She is a recipient of a Fulbright Award and a Jefferson Award for Public Service. She is the Founder and President of Animal Advocates of Greater Lafayette.

1 Introduction

Animals, Education, and Change

We are not just rather not like animals, we *are* animals.

Midgley (1979/1995, p. xxxiii) (emphasis is the author's)

Animals are an intimate and ever-present part of our human lives.[1] We share our couches and beds with our dogs and cats; we plan trips and vacations around encounters with animals at zoos, aquariums, and safaris; our children's bookshelves are full of pictures and stories about animals; and we eat animals, sometimes at every meal. No matter where we live on the planet, animals are with us inside and outside of our homes throughout our days (Brown & Nading, 2019; DeMello, 2012; Irvine, 2019; Jalongo, 2014; Lloro-Bidart & Banschbach, 2019; Melson, 2001; Pedersen, 2010; Rice & Rud, 2016; Taylor & Pacini-Ketchabaw, 2019). As Irvine (2008) writes, "Non-human animals are so tightly woven into the fabric of society that it is difficult to imagine life without them" (p. 1954).

Despite this reality, most of us learn very little about animals through our education, at least explicitly. In elementary school, we sometimes experience a class pet, and many of us dissected a frog, fetal pigs, or even a cat in middle or high school (Barr & Herzog, 2000; Hart et al., 2008; Herbert & Lynch, 2017; Oakley, 2009, 2012; Solot & Arluke, 1997). But actual learning about animals, in all their complexity, is very rare (Herzog, 2010). A small number of states in the United States mandate students receive some instruction in humane education.[2] However, there are few requirements beyond teaching kindness to animals, and in most cases that kindness is limited to pets (Arbour et al., 2009; Daly & Suggs, 2010). As a result of the lack of attention to animals in formal school curriculum, children who want to explore and learn more about animals often do so through extracurricular and recreational activities, for example through 4-H, horseback riding, and summer camps at zoos. As Ellis and Irvine (2010) argue in their qualitative study of a 4-H youth livestock program, what young people learn in these programs often serves to reproduce, not challenge, humans' power and dominion over other animals (Gillespie, 2018; Scully, 2002).[3] Another avenue for learning about animals outside of schools is through humane education programs, which are predominantly found in outreach and education departments of animal shelters. For example, the membership of the Association of Professional Humane Educators (based in the United States) is largely composed of animal shelter employees (Association of Professional Humane Educators, 2021).

DOI: 10.1201/9781003269984-1

When it comes to learning about animals, education happens outside—not inside—of schools.

Because schools do not generally teach (explicitly) about animals, educators are not the primary source of expertise about animals in our society. As someone with a PhD in education, who has studied and worked in the field of education for more than 30 years, I have observed how this curious reality is very evident in our institutional structures. For example, a student entering a teacher education program at my university can study for state-level certifications in an array of fields: language and literacy, math, science, social studies, elementary education, special education, gifted education, and a wide variety of subjects taught in secondary schools. But nowhere is there a certification in anything specifically focused on animals: while humane education is a small field of study, it is rarely, if ever, discussed in colleges of education. One of the only humane education graduate certificates offered in the United States is based in the School of Social Work at the University of Denver through their Institute for Human-Animal Connection. Teaching and learning about and for animals are largely absent from the landscape of formal schooling in the United States and our teacher education programs.

Instead of teachers, our society considers veterinarians to be the primary experts about animals. Almost 30 years ago, Tannenbaum (1993) argued that the veterinary profession needs to be at the core of any study of human–animal relationships, writing,

> Any comprehensive approach to the subject of human-animal relations must include attention to the practices and values of the veterinary profession, for it is not-nor will it ever be-social scientists, biomedical researchers, philosophers, lawyers, or politicians who exercise the greatest influence over how animals are treated. More often than the members of these groups, it is a veterinarian who must advise upon, make or carry out critical decisions regarding animals.

(p. 143)

By 2022, there are ample reasons to question Tannebaum's assertion that professions beyond veterinary medicine will never influence how animals are cared for in our society. Indeed, many of the recent shifts in societal attitudes have come from the very fields that Tannenbaum dismisses as lacking influence and power. Yet, despite this, the core of Tannebaum's assertion still resonates as true: the majority of the public turns to veterinarians for both practical medical advice and overall guidance and direction involving how to think about and relate to animals. This socialization to seeing the veterinarian as the "expert" on animals begins very early with picture books in childhood (Capucilli, 2008; MacPete, 2018). In these books, a kindly, welcoming veterinarian—often white and female—is gently examining a dog while the dog's family stands quietly in the background, watching and learning.[4] As Siegford et al. (2010) reflect, "Veterinarians are commonly regarded as the professionals with the greatest knowledge of animals. They are trusted by the public with all manner of decisions concerning animals" (p. 53).

While more recently many of us are apt to consult "Dr. Google" for medical advice for our entire family, both human and animal, much of our explicit learning (and mislearning) about animals, if it happens at all, occurs in a veterinarian's office. The most recently available statistics from the American Veterinary Medical Association (2021) indicated that more than 137 million U.S. households had either a pet cat or dog. More than 80% of households with dogs and 50% of households with cats visited a veterinarian at least once during the year. Every single one of these veterinary visits was medical but also inevitably educational for the animal's family. In 2019, almost $30 billion dollars was spent on veterinary care and another $60 billion on other products and services for pets (American Pet Product Association, 2021). The numbers of companion animals in the United States continue to increase: the American Veterinary Medical Association (2020) projects that the number of pets in the United States will climb to approximately 185 million by the year 2030.

Veterinarians are the profession that society turns to for answers about how to care for *all* animals: they are, as I have discussed elsewhere, educators, despite being untrained and unprepared for that position (Dolby & Litster, 2015). This is a huge and overwhelming responsibility for the veterinary profession. To understand the scope of the veterinary profession, begin by counting the number of animals that you personally encounter in any one day, both inside and outside your home. In addition to your pets (companion animals) and the animals that are on your plate, wildlife surrounds us (sometimes unseen) in urban, suburban, and rural areas; social media, books, television, and movies are all full of animals; and while you may not realize it there are parts of various animals in your paint, tires, cars, and hundreds of other household items (Hayes & Hayes, 2015). As humans, we are surrounded by and encounter thousands, of animals, both alive and dead, every single day of our lives. While the public may imagine all veterinarians as helpful, compassionate, and smiling broadly as they take care of a treasured cat or dog, veterinarians also care for animals who are raised and slaughtered for food, for animals who are used in research laboratories, wildlife, and those who populate zoos, aquariums, and racetracks. Veterinary knowledge is also a crucial component of human public health, working through a One Health perspective to prevent the spread of zoonotic diseases. As a worldwide movement, One Health recognizes the interconnectedness of humans, animals, and the environment, and that we are interdependent on each other for survival and to thrive and grow (One Health Commission, 2020). For expertise on all these animals, excluding the human animal, society relies on veterinarians. Most of the public has simply assumed that veterinarians know everything about animals, and veterinary schools and colleges have been the primary educational space in which teaching and learning about animals have occurred.

Thus, over a decade ago, I began to realize that if I wanted to understand how society educates/miseducates about animals, I would need to focus my research primarily on veterinary education.

CHANGING SOCIETAL PERSPECTIVES ON ANIMALS AND THE ROLE OF VETERINARY EDUCATION

Historically, the veterinary profession has, for the most part, treated animals who have value to humans. For example, horses have been used for transportation; cows, pigs, and chickens are slaughtered for food; captive orcas are used for entertainment (Jones, 2003). Companion animals are also economic drivers because of the billions of dollars that we invest in our "furry" family members (Cushing, 2020). As I develop through this book the veterinary profession is still largely governed by this worldview: animals are seen and understood through a human lens. From this perspective animals are not valued for their own intrinsic worth as sentient beings, but instead for their value, whether economic or emotional, to humans.

But the reality in our broader society is evolving quickly. Knowledge, understanding, and interest in animals are growing exponentially, fueled by new awareness of the centrality of the human–animal bond, animal welfare, animal rights, and the environment. There are global, national, and local efforts to end puppy mills, shutdown circuses and venues such as SeaWorld, end dog and horse racing, stop cat declawing, decrease or eliminate the use of animals for food and fur, eliminate gestation crates for pigs, retire primates used in laboratories, end animal testing for personal care products in corporations and laboratories, create animal shelters and communities that are "no kill," prohibit breed specific legislation that often bans "pit-bull" dogs from entire cities, establish legal personhood for animals, and hundreds more (Bekoff & Pierce, 2017; Chan, 2016; Choplin, 2018; Cushing, 2020; Dickey, 2016; Foer, 2009, 2019; Gluck, 2016; Grimm, 2014; Hegedus & Pennebaker, 2016; Jenkins & Walter, 2016; Nir & Schweber, 2017; Reese, 2018; Sunstein & Nussbaum, 2004; Wise, 2000). The public, and millions of people without veterinary degrees, are beginning to forcefully assert their own knowledge, perspectives, and opinions on animals in a growing movement for justice, including in the field of critical animal studies (Gillespie, 2018; McCance, 2013). This is a significant shift from the moment that Tannenbaum reflects on in 1993, as individuals who are not veterinarians are beginning to assume more influence and control. Amid this societal upheaval about our human relationships to animals in the 21st century, the ethical and moral challenges of being a veterinarian are heightened, reflecting the new awareness of animals in our human world. How should humans relate to animals: should we keep them as pets, lock them in zoos, dissect them, use their fur, and eat them?

In response to some of these societal shifts over the past two decades, the veterinary profession has instituted some limited internal changes. In 2011, "animal welfare" was added to the veterinary oath (Bones & Yeates, 2012). While from an outside perspective it may seem to be accepted commonsense that a veterinarian would be concerned with the welfare of animals, before 2011 the U.S. veterinary oath made no mention of it.[5] Until that time veterinarians' responsibility was to animal health but not the larger reality of that animal's world. What the public knows and understands about veterinarians is often limited to those images from children's picture books, which is far removed from the reality of the profession. As Lord et al. (2010) comment in the specific realm of animal welfare, there is a considerable gap between what the public thinks that veterinarians know and what they actually know, as education about animal welfare in veterinary colleges is either limited or non-existent. Within the profession itself, there is a strong and growing consensus that change is needed. Even more than a decade ago Lord and Walker (2009) argued, "The traditional veterinary curricula that primarily focus on animal health will no longer suffice" (p. 276). Since that time there has been considerable reflection and action on rethinking and changing the veterinary curriculum to incorporate the heightened focus on animal welfare. For example, a model curriculum for veterinary colleges and schools has been proposed, and the leading journal in veterinary medical education (*The Journal of Veterinary Medical Education*) and other journals in the field (e.g., *Anthrozoös*) regularly publish empirical research on reform in veterinary curriculum and pedagogy (Abood & Siegford, 2012; Lord et al., 2017; Menor-Campos, Diverio et al., 2019; Menor-Campos, Knight et al., 2019; Shivley et al., 2016; Siegford et al., 2010). While the original inclusion of "animal welfare" in the veterinary oath was contested, there is now emerging more sustained interest and commitment to the principle of animal welfare throughout the profession in large part in response to changing public attitudes (Dolby, 2015, 2015a, 2020; Dolby & Litster, 2015, 2019; Nolen, 2011).

Though there is a veritable mountain of literature on the education of medical doctors for humans, there is comparatively little research on veterinary education. Perhaps most significantly for this book, while medical education throughout the world has been studied by researchers from both within and outside of the medical profession, there are very few studies of veterinary education from outside of the field. Research on medical education is published in dozens of journals within the field of medicine itself and has also been studied through the disciplinary lenses of anthropology, sociology, narrative medicine (a field influenced by literature and English, see Charon, 2001), communications, history, economics, communications, and subfields of education, among many other disciplines. There are entire journals, for example, *Medical Humanities* and *Medical Anthropology Quarterly* dedicated to research and study of the medical profession by scholars who are situated outside of academic medicine. As a result, thousands of studies of medical education are published every year from scholars within *and outside* the profession. This diversity of perspectives creates rich, varied, and dynamic conversations that have been drivers of consistent and steady change and innovation in medical education.

In contrast, veterinary education is generally written about by a small number of veterinary researchers and scholars—with limited to no educational background—who research veterinary education and publish in a few journals dedicated to veterinary education. There are only a small number of published research studies and dissertations (many more than 20 years old) in the fields of sociology, anthropology, folklore, and other humanities fields (Arluke, 1997, 2004; Barr & Herzog, 2000; Herzog, 1989; Pedersen, 2013; Vermilya, 2012, 2015; Ware, 2017). Veterinary education has simply been overlooked by researchers and scholars outside of the veterinary field primarily because animals have never been as valued as humans. As society rethinks human–animal relationships and the ways in which we value animals, there is a need for more intense and sustained focus on veterinary education from the perspectives of multiple disciplines, just as has been common in medical education for many decades. As the veterinary profession changes in response to shifting societal values, it too would benefit from the diverse voices of many scholars and researchers, in multiple fields and disciplines, who care about and are committed to animals and our shared human–animal future.

AN EDUCATOR WHO STUDIES VETERINARY
EDUCATION: EXPLORING UNCHARTED WORLDS

Veterinarians, in what they say, what they do, and the decisions that they make, are educators and teachers. Despite this, there is limited interaction between these two fields: the intersecting literature that exists is largely instrumental in approach. For example, there are research studies published in educational journals that use the "tools" of education to assist the field of veterinary education to improve student retention and memorization of course material, to effectively implement group work, and to use educational technology for study and review (e.g., Barron et al., 2017; Channon et al., 2017; Dooley & Makasis, 2020). Largely absent from the literature, however, are research studies that explore veterinary education from multiple additional lenses that are central to educational research and scholarship, for example, critical, philosophical, pedagogical, sociological, ethnographic, and moral/ethical.[6] As a result, the field of education knows very little about veterinary education: there is virtually no research on these professionals who teach every day, both implicitly through their decision making and explicitly through interactions with clients and the public. What do veterinarians learn in veterinary school? What experiences, both before and during veterinary school, shape their perceptions of animals and of humans? What do they learn through their veterinary education about the critical issues facing us as a society vis-à-vis animals? How do the structures, curriculum, and pedagogies of veterinary colleges shape these experiences?

In the veterinary education community, research is published primarily (though not, of course, exclusively) in *The Journal of Veterinary Medical Education* (JVME), which is the official peer-reviewed journal of the American Association of Veterinary Medical Colleges.[7] Publications in this journal are concerned with, not surprisingly, improving veterinary education, with articles that focus on the use of applied educational approaches and learning theories (e.g., Boller et al., 2021; Scholz et al., 2013; Warren & Donnon, 2013). For example, the April 2021 issue of JVME highlights "collaborative learning" as an educational strategy. An earlier issue, in February 2021, was concerned with learning on-line and through simulations. Many of the articles in this issue were based on real life experiences during the early months of the COVID-19 pandemic, when many veterinary schools' laboratory and field-based activities were either prohibited or significantly curtailed.

From my perspective, the overwhelmingly instrumental lenses that dominate both fields are extremely limiting, avoiding the moral and ethical dilemmas that are at the core of our society's relationship with animals. For example, the important questions to ask of veterinary education revolve around whether students *should* perform terminal surgeries on dogs (or pigs, or any other animal), not *how* to perform them better, how to learn more from the experience, or how to work more effectively in a group while involved in the lesson. With a few exceptions from within the veterinary profession (e.g., Bernard Rollin's well-known and respected scholarship and research), these questions have been raised from disciplines and fields outside of veterinary medicine. While this book draws on literature from dozens of fields in the humanities, social sciences, health sciences, and natural sciences, my focus is largely pedagogical, as I approach my study from an educational perspective, one that is focusing on teaching and learning.

In this book, I expand the conversation in these two research communities through telling the complicated, fascinating stories of the experiences of a cohort of 20 veterinary students whom I followed from the year they entered veterinary school in the fall of 2015 through their graduation in the spring of 2019. Once a year—five times during their veterinary education—I met with the students individually for interviews. We discussed what brought them to veterinary education, their life experiences with animals, the moments and turning points that shaped and defined their veterinary education, the paths that they chose, the paths that they left behind either permanently or temporarily, their passions, and their lives. Over those five years, I watched as this group of young adults transformed from recent college graduates in jeans, tank tops, and flip flops to professionals in white coats ready to take their veterinary oaths. I also heard their personal stories about beloved pets who had died, their families, their engagements and marriages, and their tears as they negotiated a rigorous and often uncaring environment while also confronting their own personal and developmental challenges. Many of the students in my study had never even traveled outside of the United States before veterinary school: those stories and many more are a part of these young adults' exploration and development over their four years of veterinary education.

I use their stories as the basis for this book to map what happens to these students from the early days of veterinary school to graduation. I reflect on and analyze how their experiences during this period shaped their beliefs and perspectives about animals, their relationship with animals, their views on animal ethics and animal welfare, and their views on the veterinary profession. Through their narratives I write the story of how our society's primary teachers about animals are schooled: what they learn and do and what is absent, hidden, or simply ignored (Dolby, 2016).

The research that forms the core of this book was conducted from 2015 to 2019. However, my interest and research in veterinary education began more than a decade ago through the field of shelter medicine. As a longtime volunteer at a local animal shelter, I became interested in how animals and humans experience an animal shelter and in doing research that explores the ways in which animal health and animal welfare in a shelter environment are inseparable (Guenther, 2020). This new curiosity led me to a collaboration with the (then) director of the Shelter Animal Medicine program at my university and a survey-based research project that focused how veterinary students enrolled in a Shelter Animal Medicine class perceived and understood the concept of animal welfare (Dolby & Litster, 2015, 2019). The original research questions for this earlier study were framed solely around animal welfare given its recent addition to the veterinary oath. However, students consistently discussed animal welfare in the context of (and generally in opposition to) animal rights and thus that also became part of the study as it developed. By the time the survey research was completed and published, I had become fully immersed in the veterinary education literature and was quickly discovering its limited scope. Considering our finding (Dolby & Litster, 2015) that veterinary students see themselves as future educators, I began to design a study that would examine what our society's primary educators about animals are learning and quite critically *not* learning through their education. To be able to capture the entire story, the research was explicitly designed as both qualitative and longitudinal to provide depth and to allow me to fully tell these students' stories and explore their journey. I tell my own story in more detail in Chapter 9, "A Researcher's Tale: Making Change for Animals."

This book sits at a critical crossroads in conversations about how we teach about animals. I am situated and immersed in the world of education, education colleges, and education research and I inevitably approach my study through that lens. However, because I am fundamentally interested in how we teach and learn about animals in our society, the focus of my study takes me outside of education to a veterinary college at a university that I call Central Midwest University (a pseudonym). What veterinarians learn through their education has enormous consequences for public policy and practice. When society makes decisions about almost all ethical and moral decisions involving animals, we look to veterinarians to guide us through the complexity of these dilemmas. Should we use animals for invasive procedures in research labs; allow horse-drawn carriage rides; keep fish as pets in small tanks; boil lobsters alive; allow pet shops to sell dogs; ban backyard breeders; and eat chickens (and other animals) from confined animal feeding operations (CAFOs)? These are just a very small sample of the landscape of hundreds of ethical issues involving animal use that we as humans face every day. What veterinarians learn through their four years of veterinary education has a significant influence on how we as humans relate to animals, from public policy and decision making about the environment and animals slaughtered to food, to the most personal decisions about euthanizing companion animals. The consequences of our human relationships with animals are not minor: in contrast, how we think and approach animals in all aspects of our lives are the decisions that will define our future as human beings and the survival of the planet. The story of veterinary education is essential to our society's transforming relationships with animals, the earth, and ultimately ourselves as humans. As a result, any conversation about current and ongoing shifts in the place of animals in our society must include a meaningful engagement with what is taught, and learned in veterinary education, because veterinarians are our teachers—in many ways our sages—about animals.

The title of the book, *Learning Animals* reflects the multiple ways that I think about this interface between the fields of education and veterinary education. First, "learning" is a key concept in education, one which has a rich and contested history. "Learning" can (and often does) refer to what Freire (1970) refers to as "banking" education. Certainly, the students who participated in my research study described their experiences during their first two years of veterinary education as largely situated within this philosophical framework. In a banking approach to learning, knowledge is conceptualized as fixed and is poured or transferred (thus the "banking" metaphor) into students' heads. In direct repudiation of banking education, dozens, if not hundreds, of schools of thought and approaches to learning have emerged, including sociocultural approaches such as Dewey and Vygotsky (Popkewitz, 1998; Roth & Lee, 2007) the critical lens of Apple (1979), and multiple philosophical schools under the larger umbrella of critical pedagogy (Darder et al., 2017). Similarly, "animals" is a key concept in veterinary education: they are the objects and the patients, though their value to the veterinary profession is often dependent on their human use value (Jones, 2003). I use both words in the title as a way of placing them in dynamic conversation. The title also reflects what veterinary students do every day. They "learn animals"—always *about* animals, always *on* animals, yet rarely *with* animals. This is a largely hidden philosophical stance that is embedded in veterinary education, one that this study attempts to both reveal and unravel.

Finally, in the end, the participants in this study were, and are themselves, learning animals. As Midgley's (1979/1995) epigraph that opens this chapter reminds us, humans are also animals. That basic fact is often lost in a world system that rests on a denial of that truth. Within most veterinary models, only humans learn while animal learning is generally described as behavior or instinct. For example, undergraduate programs in animal science often have majors in the field of animal behavior. Related courses, programs, and services in veterinary colleges will frequently use the word "behavior" in titles and descriptions. Yet, fields such as cognitive ethology, which I will discuss in Chapter 7, assert that all animals (including non-human animals) learn. From this perspective, human learning is on a continuum with animal learning, following Darwin's (1871/1998) assertion that differences between species are of degree, not kind. All animals, including the human ones who participated in this study and the animals whom they learned on/about and (rarely) with, have the capacity to learn and thus to change.

OVERVIEW OF CHAPTERS

In the second chapter of this book, "Animals in Education: An Overview," I review the current landscape of research on the role of animals in education across the life spectrum, beginning with preschool and concluding with an overview of veterinary education. This chapter provides necessary context and background for the book, because the veterinary students I discuss in the chapters that follow are a product of the larger social and cultural context. They too went to elementary schools where they learned to read with stories populated by friendly animals and then ate those same animals at lunch. While there are few studies of veterinary education in the educational literature, there is a burgeoning and important literature about animals in education emerging in the K-12 context and in fields such as philosophy of education, social foundations of education, cultural studies in science education, environmental education, early childhood education, and cultural theory in education, including posthumanism (Bone, 2013; Daly & Suggs, 2010; Dolby, 2015, 2018, 2019, 2020a; Jalongo, 2014; Kuhl, 2011; Lindgren & Öhman, 2019; Lloro-Bidart, 2018; Lupinacci, 2019; Martusewicz et al., 2015; Melson, 2001; Pedersen, 2004, 2010, 2010a, 2011; Rice & Rud, 2016, 2018; Snaza & Weaver, 2015; Spannring, 2017; Taylor, 2017; Taylor & Pacini-Ketchabaw, 2019).

As the objective of this book is to engage both veterinary and educational researchers in conversations about how society educates about animals, through this chapter I situate my current research study on veterinarians and veterinary education within the larger arc of research and scholarship on animals in education. I use a chronological approach, employing the framework of "animal presences" developed by Pedersen (2011) to map how educational institutions socialize children and young adults to the contradictory messages about animals in our society. I then discuss the history of the veterinary profession, veterinary education, and current conversations in the veterinary field about professionalism and professional identity, which provide necessary context and background for the chapters that follow. Throughout, this chapter is concerned with pedagogical questions about what we as humans *learn* about animals through both formal schooling and informal institutions. In this way, veterinary education is positioned not as a separate and distinct educational entity, but as part of a sequence of educational experiences that are built on a specific philosophical approach to the human–animal relationship.

In the third chapter, "Beginnings: Contexts, Memories, and Stories" I introduce the research study and the students. I draw on the first conversations that I had with students immediately before and during the first week of their veterinary education and discuss the animal memories that students carry with them as they begin veterinary school. Using the framework of significant life experiences from the field of environmental education, I explore students' motivations for deciding to enter the veterinary profession, their early experiences with animals, and the complicated and often contradictory memories and passions as they begin their veterinary education (Altan & Lane, 2018; Chalwa, 1998; Howell & Allen, 2019). These memories from childhood formed the basis for students' motivation to enter the veterinary profession, creating divergent dynamics in which students were socialized to both bond with and separate from animals.

Chapter 4, "Encountering Animal Bodies" delves into students' first two years in veterinary school. Primarily lecture and classroom based, these years provide the foundation for their beginning socialization to their future professional identity (Armitage-Chan & May, 2019; Dolby, 2016; Freidson, 2001; Hafferty, 1991, 2009; Morris, 2012; Mossop & Cobb, 2013). The limited curricular exposure students have during these two years to actual animal bodies, both alive and dead, heightens the importance of these moments. This chapter is framed around encounters with specific animals whom students meet through their classroom experiences, including dogs, pigs, and chickens. The requirements of the curriculum in these early years mandated focused, prescribed, and controlled interactions with these animal bodies, which raised powerful emotions and ethical concerns for students. While these encounters were vital pedagogical moments for students, the veterinary curriculum suppresses these moments of contradiction and challenge leaving students to make sense of their own feelings and experiences.

Chapter 5, "Stepping Out: Learning in the Wild" explores students' experiences as they transition to their clinical years, which begin in the third year with enhanced clinical classes such as "junior surgery" and move into full-time clinical rotations during the fourth and final year of veterinary school. For the students in this study this is a liminal period as they transition from their role of student to that of veterinarian. Moving from primarily classroom and lecture-based education to actual hands-on experiences with patients and human clients in a veterinary teaching hospital and at clinical field sites throughout the world provides a heightened moment of recon-nection with animals. Students rediscover their intense emotional connection with animals and tell detailed, powerful stories of individual animals and their human companions.

Chapter 6, "Endings: There Are No Animals Here," draws on my final inter-views with students as they are about to finish their veterinary education. In these last weeks of veterinary education, students no longer "see" or "feel" animals: they have become almost exclusively focused on their own (very real) struggles, and their overwhelming negative experiences in clinical rotations. By this point, most of the participants in this study no longer can recall individual stories of animals in vivid detail nor access their own emotions about these stories. Animals, in many ways, have been erased from their learning, as they complete their veterinary education, take their veterinary oath, and begin their professional journeys.

In Chapter 7, "Telling New Stories: Toward Different Animal and Human Futures" I argue that the learning that future veterinarians do through their veteri-nary education is limited and narrow and that internal reform is only one component of the changes that are necessary. Instead, I suggest that the development and future of veterinary education would benefit from enhanced engagement with other fields outside of veterinary education. Those fields should be recognized as sites for learn-ing about and with animals. As we enter the middle decades of the 21st century, there is an opportunity to create new pedagogies, new animal stories (Pelias, 2015), and new animal "teachers" both inside and outside of the veterinary profession. I discuss promising models and practices for both nurturing and teaching animal stories draw-ing on the fields of cognitive ethology, the medical humanities, the emerging field of veterinary humanities, and my own field of educational research.

Chapter 8, "Turning Stories into New Love: Possibilities," opens conversations about the possibilities that exist to re-imagine how we learn both about and with other species, and the multiplicity, prospects, and hope that we can find in these human–animal entanglements (Gruen, 2015). I begin the chapter by discussing an example of what I term "old love" from recent veterinary education research. I then draw on current stories throughout the world, and from my own data, that point us toward new possibilities for a more humane and just future for both animals and humans. Esther the Wonder Pig, clean pet food, and McArthur's hauntingly pre-dictive reflection on oxygen, one of the opening epigraphs for this chapter, provide anchors for re-imaginings.

The book concludes with a methodological reflection in Chapter 9, "A Researcher's Tale: Making Change for Animals." I provide an overview of my own experiences with animals, humane education, and veterinary education over the past 15 years, and discuss my motivations and journey through this project. This chapter will be of particular interest to graduate and postgraduate students who are committed to using qualitative inquiry for social justice and for change.

The human struggle for justice, which reverberates strongly in the current moment, is not separate from that of other living beings. Understanding more thor-oughly what and how our society's primary teachers about animals learn through their education is a critical, though often overlooked, piece of our changing relation-ships with animals.

NOTES

1 Humans of course are also animals. As this book draws on a wide range of fields which use different terms (e.g., "animal," "non-human animal," and "more than human animals") and qualitative data from interviews, I will predominantly use "animal" for clarity. However, there will be moment where other terms are used in the literature I am discussing and as appropriate I will use those terms. I discuss humans as animals, and the implications for veterinary education and practice, in the concluding chapter of this book.

2 This research study was conducted in the United States. As a scholar, I recognize the global context of our human relationship to animals, and I use literature and research from across the world. However, an extensive international review of the literature is beyond the scope of this book and this one research study. Thus, much of the data and context provided is based in the United States.

3 4-H (head, heart, hand, and health) is a U.S.-based youth development organization. Founded in 1902; 4-H historically has served largely rural areas of the United States. Today, 4-H has six million members in the United States, and the programs are administered by cooperative extension offices at over 100 public universities. 4-H international is a related network of independent 4Hs, serving seven million young people in more than 50 nations.

4 The representation of veterinarians in children's picture books and early readers is beginning to change. For example, see Driscoll (2018) for a more diverse perspective on the profession, including race, gender, and possible specializations.

5 For a fascinating comparative and international analysis of veterinary oaths from multiple countries, see Bones and Yeates (2012).

6 There are exceptions, most notably the work of Pedersen (2013).

7 In April 2021, the name of the association changed from the Association of American Veterinary Medical Colleges to the American Association of Veterinary Medical Colleges. This shift recognizes that, in practice, the association includes veterinary colleges from across the globe, not solely in the United States or the Americas.

2 Animals in Education
An Overview

The perspective and worldview that I use throughout my analysis of the animal curriculum is informed by my positioning within a critical sociology of education, an academic subfield in education that I have worked within since my PhD research in a desegregated high school in Durban, South African in 1996 (Dolby, 2001). As a scholar, I am primarily interested in how people negotiate, make sense of, operate within, and resist the larger political, social, cultural, economic, and national structures that create the realities of our modern world. As I have written about in dozens of publications, people do not simply reproduce the structures within which they are born. Instead, they actively remake and produce their identities, as agents of transformation (Dolby & Dimitriadis, 2004; Weis et al., 2011; Willis, 1977).

Given my background in critical sociology of education, as I began to read and do research in the subfield of animals in education, I was immediately drawn to the related field of animals and society, located primarily within sociology. As Irvine (2008) writes, "non-human animals contribute so much to what we call 'society' that their exclusion from sociology amounts to a glaring omission" (p. 1955). The reality is similar in educational research: animals are always present, though rarely included in analysis of education. They constitute, in many and various ways, a silent "hidden" curriculum that we are only now beginning to unearth (Giroux & Purpel, 1983). Theoretically, my research and scholarship in this book sits at the crossroads of animals, society, and education: the three are always already interlinked and intertwined. Animals are constitutive elements of society and education (in multiple ways, of course, as humans are also animals). Society and education are also mutually informed, both shaping how we as humans relate to non-human animals.

Pedersen (2011) provides a broad outline of what she terms "animal appearance" in education, a framework I use and expand on to probe the reproductive, pedagogical aspects of the animal curriculum. Pedersen identities three themes (or what she refers to as "appearances") that dominate the animal curriculum: animals as sites of sentimentality, animals as teaching and learning tools, and animals (and more broadly, animality) as a trope and antithesis of "the human" and humanity (p. 12).

In the early years of schooling, the presence of animals is framed by sentimentality, affection, and care. In preschools and elementary schools, animals are everywhere. Most children's books feature animals, stuffed animals are everywhere, the walls of daycares and schools are plastered with pictures and posters of animals to help teach numbers and letters, children's clothing is covered with animals, and children's movies, such as Disney, feature talking, singing, and thinking animals. This abundance of animals infused into the daily lives of small children is so common as to be unremarkable to parents and teachers—it simply *is*. As Pedersen (2011) asserts,

DOI: 10.1201/9781003269984-2

this animal curriculum in the lives of young children is governed by the principle of sentimentality,

> In this context animals themselves are not the primary focus of interest; rather, they become carriers of normative messages connected to moralizing or socializing processes that are thought to be more easily internalized by children if presented in the form of animal imagery.
>
> **(p. 13)**

Melson (2001) suggests that children, like all humans, have a natural attraction to animals. She draws on Wilson's (1984) biophilia thesis, which theorizes that human evolution is linked to our relationship with other animals as our survival as a species is dependent on them. Melson writes,

> Biophilia depicts children as born assuming a connection with other living things. . . . Children readily access animals as material in the development of a sense of self. Every human child begins life situated in what adults call "the animal world".
>
> **(pp. 19–20)**

Children gradually unlearn this natural affinity for animals, internalizing the perspective that humans are distinct from and have dominion over animals (Myers, 2013; Scully, 2002; Timmerman & Ostertag, 2011). As they grow older, children begin to understand that adults sort animals into different categories. Melson (2001) reflects, "Children grapple with a complicated, often contradictory, mix of social codes governing animals and their treatment. There are creatures incorporated as family members, stamped out as pests, saved from extinction, and ground into Big Macs" (p. 21). Of course, the reality that the hamburger on a child's plate at lunchtime is the same creature that goes "moo" or "cluck" is generally not remarked upon, as adults have accepted and internalized the cultural messages about the multiple roles of animals in human lives at different stages (Herzog, 2010).[1]

Children begin to understand that it is acceptable to treat animals differently, depending on their human use value. As Rule and Zhbanova (2012) observe, "Many children treat non-pet animals with little respect. It is not uncommon to see a child stomping insects on a sidewalk or boasting about how he/she observed a snake or spider being killed" (p. 229). Children learn early in life that sentimentality extends only to *some* animals. Furthermore, they are schooled to make a distinction between Maisy the mouse in their picture book and the real-life mouse in their kitchen. Maisy is approachable, human-like, and their friend and teacher. The mouse in their kitchen is, in essence, a totally different creature. It has no resemblance to Maisy, and it is acceptable to trap (often painfully) and kill that animal. Though the same animal, one is understood and accepted as a friend, and one is a pest.

In early childhood and elementary education, animals are often carriers of particular interests-for example, helping children to learn to read, instead of being the focus of interest themselves (Pedersen, 2010, 2011). When deliberate teaching about animals occurs, the curriculum is saturated with messages about animals and their proper and subordinate relationship to humans. For example, zoos are a popular destination for class field trips as they are purposefully designed to be educational and at the same time, fun and engaging. Yet, zoos are at the center of a vigorous debate about how we as humans relate to animals, and whether it is morally acceptable to hold animals captive (Pierce & Bekoff, 2018; Safina, 2018; Shapiro, 2018). From an educational perspective, there are important questions to ask about what zoos teach children about their relationship to animals. In commenting on an early childhood book about zoos, Timmerman and Ostertag (2011) ask, "Does a book about zoo animals teach children to wonder about how long a giraffe's neck is, or does it teach them that it is normal and natural for humans to cage animals?" (p. 64).[2] Thus, while a trip to the zoo might be undertaken with an intended curriculum related to experiencing animals in real life, there is another, most likely longer lasting, lesson about animals and what is acceptable treatment and practice.

While classroom zoo trips are sporadic in elementary school, classroom pets are often a part of the daily lives of many children (People for the Ethical Treatment of Animals, 2014; Rud & Beck, 2003). Pets are included in classroom settings for pleasure, enjoyment, and stress reduction; to teach responsibility and caring for another life; and to provide children with the opportunity to learn about the life cycle and what is often termed "animal behavior." These lessons can and do happen spontaneously, as the pets experience naturally occurring changes (Rud & Beck, 2003; Zasloff et al., 1999). However, classroom pets also serve to transition children from seeing and understanding animals as purely sites of sentiment to understanding them as objects that are also used for teaching and learning. For example, the panda at the zoo and the rabbit in the classroom are both cute and cuddly: it is easy for children to see them as "friends." At the same time, their presence and use in an educational setting sends an additional message about animals, that animals can be used for teaching and learning and that they can also be objectified so that humans can learn *from* them. Thus, the school as an institution uses its societal role to position the animals within its walls in certain ways. In school, students learn to navigate these contradictory lessons. For example, children might draw a picture of their family that includes their beloved dog or cat in the morning, while later in the day they would pick up a notebook and record observations of the class guinea pig, Harold, for their science lesson. Through doing this, they see Harold not solely as a friend and companion but as an object to be studied.[3]

At the middle and high school level, sentimentality disappears as students move into Pedersen's second identified "presence," seeing animals—both alive and dead—as teaching and learning tools. Animal dissection is the central socializing practice at this stage, and as Solot and Arluke (1997) argue, it is one of the most significant ways that "schools socialize students to reproduce the perspective of modern Western science and the kind of human-animal relationship it implies" (p. 30). Pedersen (2011) also notes the centrality of dissection, writing, "One conspicuous step in the process of transforming the animal into a scientific object is making its body available for experimentation work" (p. 16). In a seminal essay defending the practice of dissection, McInerney (1993) argues, "The science classroom, perhaps more than any other site of learning, should provide students the intellectual tools to recognize and challenge fallacious arguments and false sentiment" (p. 277). Here, McInerney clearly asserts that feeling "sentiment" about animals is unscientific and the place for children to begin to abandon these illogical ideas is the science classroom. His defense of dissection reinforces Solot and Arluke's (1997) argument that the overarching objective of dissection is not the learning outcomes of cutting open a dead pig to learn about pig biology (and its similarities to human biology) but to be able to replace the sentimentality of childhood feelings toward animals with the detachment of emerging adulthood. While more recently prominent scientists, such as leading primatologist de Waal (2001), have openly challenging the idea of the "unfeeling scientist" as a caricature that needs to be dismantled, such beliefs and attitudes persist in the broader educational landscape.

Solot and Arluke (1997) discuss their qualitative, observational study of sixth grade children experiencing their first dissection, in this case of a fetal pig, "As students develop strategies to cope with their initial ambivalence and 'squeamishness', they redefine the nature of animals and reduce their identification with them" (p. 30). Solot and Arluke document the multiple ways that the students curtail and contain their emotions and their innate understanding that the dead pig they are dissecting was once alive and—moreover—just a few years ago had been a friend and companion and a frequent presence in books, posters, and movies. Throughout the dissection, students also begin the process not solely of distracting themselves, but of deliberately and clearly turning the animal into a non-animal or an object. This process is reinforced by the teacher who focuses the students on the pig's biology instead of the moral and ethical questions involved. For example, as students begin to search for specific organs during the dissection lab, the pig is transformed into a "biological puzzle" (p. 35) with the focus shifted to parts instead of the whole. The process of turning animals into objects is also reproduced in the U.S. National Science Teacher's Association's (2008) position statement on the *Responsible Use of Live Animals and Dissection in the Science Classroom*. Throughout the document, "animals" refers to living beings. In contrast, dead animals are referred to as "specimens" (instead of, for example, dead animals). This linguistic move turns the dead animal into an inanimate object, thus erasing any possible sentimentality.[4]

By high school, most students have experienced a dissection. In the U.S. context, Hart et al. (2008) estimate approximately 20 million animals are used in educational settings each year—mostly for dissections. So common is the practice that Hart et al. (2008) open Chapter 1 of their book with the statement, "Almost all readers will recall dissecting a frog, rat, or fetal pig in junior high or high school" (p. 1). Because initial exposure to dissection generally occurs in middle school, high school students encountering dissection know what to expect and have developed strategies for emotional distancing and justification. Barr and Herzog (2000), in their study of a high school fetal pig dissection lab, indicate that 11 of the 17 students in the class (65%) either agreed or strongly agreed with the statement, "I have no ethical problems with dissection" (p. 60), and 12 of the 17 students indicated that they enjoyed the dissection. By this juncture, most students had come to accept dissection as a common practice. Barr and Herzog witnessed students taking their own initiatives to minimize their emotions and feelings about the animals' death: for example, they would often drape the faces of cats and fetal pigs. Faces, of course, are powerful symbols of individuality, and the reality that the cat they are dissecting is no different from the one who will sleep on their pillow at home that night. Here, the students continue the lessons they had learned in middle school: that the animals can exist simultaneously in two categories: family member at home and object for teaching and learning at school.

As students edge closer to adulthood, they begin to internalize the perspective that animals are fundamentally different from humans, humans are superior, and that animals can be used to further human aims and objectives, a philosophical position that is central to the contemporary veterinary field. Anthropomorphism becomes something to be feared, instead of a "powerful tool" (de Waal, 2001, p. 40) to understand animals. By the time that students enter university and post-graduate education, they recognize that it is unacceptable to even discuss the ethical and moral issues involved in killing animals for human purposes. Holley, in her study of doctoral student identity in a neuroscience laboratory (2009), discusses the experience of one student, Victor, who had an undergraduate degree in computer science and no previous sustained experience in an animal research lab. She writes, "Not only did Victor have a lack of experience with animals, but he also found the topic to be taboo in his laboratory. No one talked about the ethical or emotional challenges that might arise from such practices" (p. 583). As Holley explains, lab orientation included extensive discussion of access codes, biosafety, and required training. Yet, there were no conversations about the animals used in the lab, of the emotional or ethical issues that might arise from research on animals, and the general requirement that animals be euthanized after research is concluded. Holley (2009) reports that Jason, another student in the lab, told her,

> You kill [an animal] just to see his eye, and [some animals are] 99% genetically similar to you, and in neuroscience there is not much discussion about this. They kill animals, because that is the thing to do. And there is not much of an ethical debate. [The program director] teaches a seminar on bioethics, but there is not much discussion in the lab.

(p. 584)

Jason's concern is consistent with that expressed by Gluck (2016), a prominent primatologist who began to question, and finally stop, research on primates. Gluck (2016) writes,

> The problem is that developing an informed moral identity is far down on the list of priorities for most people training for and entering scientific and professional careers. For too many, ethics training remains an optional adjunct or a tangential box-checking requirement. Without the encouragement to see themselves in moral terms and subject their decisions to serious ethical reflection, it is far too easy for young scientists to simply absorb and internalize the established herd consensus, the impoverished ethical framework that surrounds them at every step of their education and training.

(p. 284)

As Gluck observes, "herd consensus" dominates in biomedical and scientific fields. I would include veterinary medicine (and my own field of educational research) under this umbrella. It is painfully difficult to question the overwhelming consensus around the table, in the classroom, or in the lab. Even raising the question—as the student in Holley's (2009) study wished to do—seems impossible. Yet, as I have traced, the socialization to ways of seeing/not seeing animals starts much earlier in childhood, elementary school, the science classroom, and the lunchroom. By the time the students in my study have reached the point of deciding to apply to veterinary school, they are, for the most part, fully socialized not to ask hard questions of themselves, their society, or the profession they are choosing to enter.

VETERINARY EDUCATION: A HISTORICAL OVERVIEW

Deciding to become a veterinarian requires a commitment to many years of formal schooling and often significant debt upon graduation. The average starting salary for a veterinarian in 2019 was $70,045. Eighteen percent of students graduated with no debt, but for the 82% who took out loans, the average amount borrowed for veterinary school was an astounding $183,302 (American Veterinary Medical Association, 2020a). Students in my study who did not take out loans to attend veterinary school would often discuss it with me during our conversations, but also mention that they did not tell their classmates as they felt guilty about their loan-free life when others were burdened with debt. Despite these financial realities, the number of applicants to veterinary schools continues to increase. For example, from 2019 to 2020, the number of applications to the 44 members of the American Association of Veterinary Medical Colleges increased 19%, from 8645 applications in 2019 to 10,273 in 2020.[5] This follows years of regular growth in applications of 6–7% (American Veterinary Medical Association, 2020).[6]

Admission to veterinary schools and colleges, like their counterparts for human patients (medical schools and colleges) is extremely competitive. While the American Association of Veterinary Medical Colleges (AAVMC) has 54 members, only 33 of those are located in the United States, with the remainder in Canada, Europe, the Caribbean, Australia, Korea, and New Zealand. Not all of these institutions have Doctorate of Veterinary Medicine (DVM) programs: as of this writing, there were 46 DVM programs among members of the AAVMC. Because of the high demand for places in veterinary schools, they are one of the few graduate schools that are in expansion mode throughout the United States. For example, in 2020, the University of Arizona opened a veterinary college and Arkansas State, among other institutions, has explored public–private partnerships to open a veterinary college on its campus.

Veterinary schools, licensure, and state regulation in the United States began in the late 1800s.[7] The American Veterinary Medical Association (AVMA) was founded in 1863 and the first veterinary college in the United States was established in 1879 at Iowa State University, with the first four-year professional degree offered there beginning in 1903. Before that time, and during the considerable period of transition to a fully professional field, a "veterinarian" was simply anyone who claimed that title and offered their services to treat animals, generally horses (Jones, 2003). Horse health was vital to the U.S. economy: the veterinary profession grew and thrived through keeping horses alive and healthy enough to work.

As veterinarian licensure became more common and accepted, there was steady demand for medical care for animals that would be slaughtered for food, particularly beef cattle, sheep, and pigs, both in rural areas and in the extensive stockyards of cities such as Chicago. Situated at the hub of railroad lines running east and west, the Union Stock Yards in Chicago grew to be the largest animal slaughter and meat-packing operation in the world for many decades, stretching to 375 acres and containing 2300 animal pens. This intense, confined situation for animals raised for slaughter was considerably different from what had come before. In rural areas, animals destined for slaughter had more space, which curtailed the spread of disease. Maintaining "herd health" and preventing the spread of disease in urban stockyards became critical not just for animal health, but for humans. An outbreak that threatened the meat supply or a zoonotic disease that could potentially sicken hundreds of thousands of people could be crippling. Veterinarians were hired to treat animals not because of concern for animal suffering or welfare, but within the scope of animals' economic value to individual owners, and society's need to protect public health and avoid financial devastation. In 1884, the U.S. federal government recognized the importance of preventing disease outbreaks that could threaten the food supply and human health through establishing The Bureau of Animal Industry (BAI) to oversee and regulate this critical area of the growing economy.

The establishment of the BAI became a major turning point for the direction of veterinary education and the veterinary profession in the United States. As automobiles replaced horses in the late 1800s and early 1900s, applications and enrollments to veterinary schools began to falter.[8] By the beginning of the 20th century, applications had plummeted, falling over 75% between 1914 and 1924 (Jones, 2003, p. 49). With few choices available, veterinary schools accepted the increasing dominance of the BAI to the profession: there were no other options for a secure path to employment for graduates. The public health orientation and mandate of the BAI dominated the veterinary curriculum in the decades that followed with a focus on parasitology, bacteriology, immunology, pathology, and physiology (Jones, 2003, p. 54). As I will discuss in Chapter 4, the contemporary veterinary curriculum still reflects this long-ago influence of the BAI, both in curriculum and in the pedagogical focus on memorization.

After World War II, veterinarians were integral to numerous public health initiatives that moved dairy cows and chickens out of people's backyards and into large, animal agriculture operations, thus establishing federal oversight and regulation of the raising, use and slaughtering of animals for food. This shift was critical not solely for human and animal health: it also changed society's relationship to animals that were used for food. No longer was there a cow in the backyard that was the family's source of milk, or chickens kept for their eggs, or to be slaughtered and cooked for supper. Now, the milkman delivered dairy products, or they were purchased in a store. Animals were only slaughtered and butchered in approved and inspected facilities. With these shifts, veterinary practices and mindsets also changed, as veterinarians who cared for large animals began to focus on the health of the group and to think about the species, instead of the unique needs of one animal.

Companion animal health had historically been only a tiny, insignificant part of the veterinary profession. Dogs, and sometimes cats, became increasingly popular as pets in the post-World War II era, as the U.S. economy began to boom in the 1940s and especially the 1950s. The development of preventative medicine for parasites such as fleas allowed dogs and cats inside human homes: slowly, dogs and cats began to move from a doghouse in the backyard or roaming the neighborhood to coveted inside spots on the couch and the bed. This additional time spent with humans began to intensify affection, concern, and love. Small animal companion medicine grew as a field and the standardization of annual vaccinations and exams began to create a stable and growing client base. In 1953, the U.S. federal government disbanded the BAI, dividing its responsibilities among numerous government agencies. With the BAI gone, there was no longer a secure, predictable path to employment available to veterinary graduates and its centralized influence over the veterinary field diminished.

By the last decades of the 20th century, the U.S. public regarded veterinarians as primarily doctors for pets: this is a startling and historically abrupt shift for a profession that had started the century as doctors for horses and livestock. As the companion animal side of the veterinary profession boomed, veterinarians cooperated with other pet industries that produced food, toys, and various supplies (crates, leashes, litter, etc.) to cross-promote services and products (Jones, 2003). These industry connections are still vital, if at times controversial, components of both the veterinary profession and veterinary education today (Dally, 2011; Dowers et al., 2015; Schoenfeld-Tacher et al., 2016). As the veterinary profession shifted to first accommodate and then encourage medical services for companion animals, supporting the human–animal bond became a growing component of veterinary practice as humans needed to emotionally value their companion animal in order to justify paying for medical services (Knesl et al., 2016). The increasing focus on the human–animal bond in veterinary medicine has also fueled the growth of specialized veterinary hospitals, particularly in the area of small animal medicine, with medical services that often parallel those available to humans, such as oncology, ophthalmology, gastroenterology, neurology, and cardiology. Pfizer, which has had an animal health division focused primarily on agricultural needs since 1952, launched a separate animal health company, Zoetis, in 2013, becoming the world's largest public traded company in this sector. Zoetis develops pharmaceuticals for animals across the spectrum with an entire division devoted specifically to pets.

Historically, veterinary practice in the United States has been tightly tied to the economy. Veterinary care and the priorities of the profession have reflected the role of animals, and animal products, in economic growth and development. Until quite recently, "love" for animals, or wanting to help prevent animal suffering would have been a somewhat odd motivation for becoming a veterinarian. Thus, it is perfectly logical, given this historical context, that the U.S. veterinarian's oath, established by the AVMA in 1954, included solely protection of "animal health." Animal health was seen as vital not for the animal's sake, but for the human whose livelihood, and perhaps very life, was dependent on that animal. In the post-World War II period, the rise in demand for small animal and companion veterinarians jumpstarted a long process—still evolving today—of beginning to question and rethink what it means, at core, to be a veterinarian. The inclusion of the protection of "animal welfare" in the oath beginning in 2011 raised additional questions about the veterinarian's purpose, and the cross-cutting tensions between privileging human versus animal interests (Tannenbaum, 1993). These questions and concerns were compounded by an increased focus toward the end of the 20th century on issues of "non-technical competence" within the veterinary profession, including such skills as communication with colleagues, staff and clients, financial management and business practices, leadership, and ethics (Burns et al., 2006; Lloyd & King, 2004). These softer skills were seen as critical components of building the business and financial side of veterinary practices and thus raising veterinary salaries, which through the 1980s and 1990s lagged far behind those of similarly educated professionals in the United States (Cron et al., 2000).

Yet, focusing only on skills as educational outcomes in veterinary school was very limited, and threatened to diminish the prestige of the profession at a moment that it was concerned with increasing its status and thus veterinarians' incomes. As a result, veterinary educators began to explore the development of veterinary professionalism as an educational outcome that would move beyond the skills approach (Mossop & Cobb, 2013). In the final section of this chapter, I turn to that literature and discussion, as it both shapes and limits the conversations that are possible within a veterinary education environment.

PROFESSIONALISM AND VETERINARY IDENTITY

Drawing on the voluminous literature in medical education on teaching professionalism, Mossop and Cobb (2013) provide a benchmark literature review of multiple approaches to the teaching of professionalism in veterinary education, emphasizing that balancing human and animal priorities are a challenge that is unique to veterinary medicine. In addition, they note the overlap between ethics and professionalism in both the veterinary and medical education curriculum, and the ongoing conversations and tensions as to whether these are inherently linked or separate areas of inquiry and teaching. Indeed, the new literature on veterinary students' attitudes toward animal welfare/ethics is largely separate from the professionalism discussions that abound, creating considerable distance between these conversations (Abood & Siegford, 2012; Colombo et al., 2016; Dolby, 2020; Hazel et al., 2011; Izmirli et al., 2014; Johnstone et al., 2019; Lord & Walker, 2009; Lord et al., 2010; Menor-Campos, Diverio et al., 2019). More recently, Armitage-Chan and May (2019) have examined a move within the medical education literature to refocus attention away from the practice of *teaching* professionalism to providing curriculum support to aid students in the process of identity formation (my emphasis). They suggest that this literature can be used to develop a model that is appropriate for the veterinary education environment.

Yet, from a sociological perspective that is concerned with the relationship between animals and society, these intense conversations about the development of a professional veterinary identity barely consider the central conflicts and tensions that are central to veterinary practice today, which rotate around the place of the animal. The "herd consensus" that Gluck (2016) identifies in biomedical and other subfields of animal laboratory research extends to veterinary medicine: asking difficult questions about if and how veterinarians should participate in educational and professional activities that harm animals and contribute to animal suffering are often considered to be outside of the realm of acceptable professional discourse. As I will explore in future chapters, many of the students who participated in this study indicated that the *only* conversations that they had about the issues regarding the animal suffering that they witnessed and at times participated in through veterinary school happened in their yearly meetings with me. This was true for students who found these practices ethically and morally worrisome, and those who fully accepted that animal suffering and death for human purpose is justifiable. Instead of engaging with these issues through their education, the students in my study existed in a professional environment which seemed to pretend that, in broad strokes, conflicts between human and animal interests either did not exist or were largely irrelevant to veterinary education. Students might have a conversation with a roommate, friend, family member, or spouse/partner about, for example, the ethics of eating animals. Yet, they separated these conversations, and this side of themselves (the "human" side) from the professional identity mantle that they were expected to assume as they entered veterinary school.

This conflict between their "human" and "professional" identity is at the core of the student stories that I discuss in this book. In the field of medical education, Goldberg (2008) provides a trenchant and relevant critique of professionalism, one that—with some limits—is central to the analysis that I develop in this research study. Goldberg argues that in medical education, humanism has been paired with, and in many cases, largely subsumed under the mantle of professionalism. Goldberg, however, carefully demarcates the boundaries between the two. He writes,

> While humanism appeals to universal values, professionalism is rooted in the local traditions of a group whose self-identity lies primarily in its distinction from the surrounding lay community. . . . Humanism emanates from a primary duty towards humanity. Professionalism, on the other hand, relates only indirectly to society. Enhancement of the profession's service to society might be a result, but professionalism itself is aimed primarily towards protecting the autonomy and integrity of the profession for its own sake.

(pp. 716–717)

Goldberg interrogates what he terms the "rough edge" of humanism and professionalism through examining the experiences of medical students as they confront the many contradictions between their internalized lay/humanist perspective, and the professional mantle they are expected to embrace on their path to becoming a doctor. In conclusion, Goldberg argues that instead of pushing the "slogan" of professionalism in medical education, the field should commit to embracing and engaging the conflicts between the poles of humanism and professionalism. He writes,

> We serve our students best by keeping their tensions alive rather than masking them. . . . Let them learn to subordinate their medical, professional identity to their essential human character, for our goal is physicians who see their medicine as part of a commitment to humanism, not physicians who superficially incorporate values of humanism into their picture of medicine.

(p. 721)

The intellectual center of my study embraces Goldberg's fundamental insight, translated into the veterinary environment. What is critical, from my perspective, is not a detached professionalism that is responsible only to itself and the perpetuation of the veterinary profession, but instead opening the profession to grappling with the very human conflicts about the relationship to animals that are at its core. As a field, the veterinary profession's roots are firmly tied to positioning animal needs within human priorities and to serve human interests. Yet, that belief system is increasingly questioned and challenged by new attitudes and perspectives, new scientific research, and new global realities, such as climate change. To be able to fully engage the stories and lives of the students who participated in my research study, I use Goldberg's work to study the "rough edge" that my students inhabit as they move through their veterinary education. Like Goldberg, I am interested in hearing and understanding how students make sense of their conflicted experiences with animals during their veterinary education, instead of burying these discussions. I try to see, in all their complexity, the very *human* animals that the participants in this study—and indeed, all of us—are, and to navigate this space of uncertainty with them.

NOTES

1 Indeed, this was evident to me during my daughter's kindergarten class trip to a local farm, about a decade ago. The farm raises and slaughters animals for food, and the guide talked very openly with the children about that reality. My daughter was the only child there who was aware of the connection between the animal "chicken" in front of her and "chicken" that is often on the dinner plate. While I was very pleased to see the guide talking openly with the children about this, many other parents were notably uncomfortable, and tried to deflect the conversation into other areas. I can hope, but not assume, that there is increased comfort with these discussions today.

2 These questions about what is "normal" and "natural" are also evident in aspects of children's popular culture. For example, in response to public pressure, in 2018, Nabisco changed the design of the box of the beloved children's snack, animal crackers. Previously, the animals were displayed behind bars and now they roam freely. At the time, I was teaching my undergraduate course, *Animals, Society, and Education*. I showed the students the contrasting images of the old and new box designs, and we discussed the different messages that are conveyed about the relationship between animals and humans.

3 The behaviorist mindset (Irvine, 2008) that undergirds this type of observation is significantly different from the type of observation that is used in the field of cognitive ethology, which I discuss in Chapter 7.

4 As of this writing, the 2008 document is the most current and updated position statement from this organization.

5 As noted in Chapter 1, the Association of American Veterinary Medical Colleges changed its name to the American Association of Veterinary Medical Colleges in April 2021. Updates to the name and website links were ongoing during the writing of this book. Thus, readers may find that links/references have been changed. The name used in the in-text citation and references reflect the Association's name at the time of publication and/or access.

6 This research study was completed before the COVID-19 pandemic. It is important to note that within the growth of pet adoptions during COVID in 2020 and 2021, the veterinary

profession, particularly in the companion animal specialty area, is facing extraordinary demand for its services, staff shortages, and decreased unemployment (American Veterinary Medical Association, 2020b).

7 While beyond the scope of this book, the history of veterinary medicine in the European context and its complicated relationship to human medicine is fascinating and a current area of considerable new scholarship. For example, see Gardiner (2014), Heintzman (2018), Mitsuda (2017), and Woods (2017). This scholarship is referenced briefly in Chapter 4, in the discussion of students' initial encounters with animals during their first two years of veterinary school.

8 The replacement of horses with automobiles also led to an exponential rise in horse slaughter, and as Jones (2003) discusses, a veterinarian-supported campaign to eat horse meat, which was (and in large part, still is) a cultural taboo in the United States. See also Vermilya (2012).

3 Beginnings
Contexts, Memories, and Stories

I met the students who participated in this study in August 2015. Just starting veterinary school, they were full of nervous energy and excitement. Many of them had dreamt of this day for more than a decade: most could not believe that they had made it into a vet school and were just four years away from their goal. Some students had just finished undergraduate degrees, others had returned to school after a break working in the veterinary field or traveling. A small number were part of a special program that allowed them to transfer to the veterinary college after completing the first two years of their undergraduate degree.

In this chapter, I introduce the research and the participants, and present some of the stories, memories, and experiences that shape these students' lives as they begin their journey.

THE RESEARCH STUDY AND PARTICIPANTS

The students who participated in the study that forms the foundation for this book attended veterinary school at Central Midwest University (CMU) from 2015 to 2019. Because this book is based on interviews from a small, qualitative study, I use a pseudonym for the institution to protect the privacy of the students involved. The stories told here are intimate, personal, and particular: to be able to share the students' experiences in meaningful and vivid detail, I must use a pseudonym.

Students who were part of the entering Central Midwest University veterinary class of 2019 were contacted via email several weeks before the semester started to ask if they were willing to participate in this study through their four years of veterinary school. To ensure a diversity of participants, I also verbally spoke with students at their orientation session before the semester started. Of the students who started veterinary school that year, 40 of them volunteered to participate, slightly less than half of the entering class. Of those 40, I chose 20 participants, with the objective of trying to ensure diversity in gender, race, and nationality. Seventeen of the 20 participants (85%) were women. At the time of this study approximately 76% of entering veterinary students were female (Association of American Veterinary Colleges, 2015). The profession has become increasingly dominated by women and is currently the most feminized of comparable health sciences professions (Irvine & Vermilya, 2010; Lincoln, 2010).

Fifteen participants identified as white (75%), two as black, one as Latina, one as white and Native American, and one as Chinese (Chinese national): thus, 25% of the participants were from underrepresented groups. Nationally, 14% of entering

DOI: 10.1201/9781003269984-3

veterinary students were from underrepresented groups at the time of this study (Association of American Veterinary Colleges, 2015).

As students enter veterinary school, they must indicate an intended track of specialization. It was important for me to ensure that all potential tracks were represented in this study. Thus, as I made selections for participants, I was mindful that I needed to balance representation of the different tracks alongside considerations of race, gender, and nationality. At the time of this research, students at Central Midwest University could choose among multiple possible tracks of specialization: equine (2 participants), food animal (2), small animal (8), companion animal (horses and small animal) (2), large animal (horses and food animal) (1), mixed animal (6), and non-practice (research or industry) track (2). As Vermilya (2012, 2015) discusses, these "tracks" are socially constructed: animals who do not fit clearly and neatly in a track are representative of the human struggle over our relationship with other species. For example, Vermilya focuses on horses as a border animal in her research. In my study, pigs emerged as an animal that troubled these borders. In Chapter 4, I expand on the social construction and meaning of these tracks in the larger social and cultural context as I discuss the veterinary curriculum. Because students do not formally commit to a track until later in their degree program, the tracks indicated represent students' interests at the time of the first interview, though as expected some students' interests and thus track did change through veterinary school. At the beginning of the study, several students indicated more than one track/interest, thus the number of tracks is greater than the number of participants.

I started my interviews in August, immediately before and during the students' first weeks of vet school. Subsequently, each participant was interviewed once a year though the timing of the interviews changed somewhat as students entered their final clinical year. During their clinical year, students are required to complete 17 three-week clinical rotations. Some students spend several consecutive rotations off campus at locations throughout the United States and the world, obtaining experience in specialty areas that were not available at CMU. As a result, I had to change the scheduling of these later interviews to accommodate students' availability for face-to-face interviews at their home campus.

Students received a $25 gift card for a national retailer for the first four interviews and a $35 gift card for the final interview in April/May 2019, as students graduated. I started with 20 student participants in 2015, which was five more than my original target of 15 students. While 20 students completed the first interview, one declined to participate in subsequent interviews. Her first interview was powerful and emotional. I include excerpts from it in this chapter, but her story does not continue through the remainder of this book. One additional student completed the first four interviews but did not respond to repeated requests for a final interview. As I was unable to contact her, her story is absent from Chapter 6. In total, 18 students completed all five interviews. The interviews lasted between 45 minutes and 2 hours. Not surprisingly, the interviews were shorter toward the beginning of the study when students were just getting to know me. In contrast, the final interviews were often very long, detailed, and frequently tearful. Toward the end of the final interview, some of the students wanted to know when I would be contacting them for their interview next year as they had come to see our yearly check-in as a core component of their veterinary education and early entry into the profession. Strong emotion was a constant part of these conversations, both for the students and often for me, as I struggled to hear and respect the students, their stories, and realities, while at the same time often vehemently disagreeing with their positions on animal welfare and rights.

As an educator who has worked in the field of multicultural education for 30 years, I am accustomed to having powerful and emotional reactions and disagreements with both students whom I teach and participants in my research studies. Part of the difficult work of change is to be able to listen to the experiences of people whose choices we disagree with, so we understand the realities that have led them to those conclusions. In my earlier book, I detail my own journey and my application of the concept of empathy to be able to work with and successfully teach students in my multicultural education classes over the past three decades (Dolby, 2012). I use many of the same principles here in this book as a researcher who is also, inevitably, a teacher. My own story is discussed in more detail in the final chapter ("A Researcher's Tale: Making Change for Animals").

Most of the students who participated in this research study excelled in science in high school and college and all had extensive experience with animals, which is a key requirement for admission to veterinary school. But as I discovered through my interviews, few of the students had well-developed critical thinking and reflection skills. Their exposure to fields where these skills would be developed, such as history, political science, philosophy, English, and related humanities and social science fields, was extremely limited. Students were well versed in scientific fields but had little to no education that would allow them to place science within a broader cultural, social, and political context (Knorr-Cetina, 1999; Kuhn, 1962). This turned into (somewhat anticipated) complication of the research, because often I was the only person who had *ever* asked my participants what they thought about intricate and multi-layered issues related to animal welfare and animal rights. For example, most students had memorized a textbook definition of animal welfare for their admission interview to veterinary school, but they had little understanding beyond that and often could not reflect in a meaningful way on the definition they had memorized. As a result, our yearly interviews were undoubtedly also educational for students, exposing them to new questions that they had not previously considered.

FRAMEWORKS: METHODOLOGY AND THEORY

Multiple methodological and theoretical frameworks inform this research project. This research was designed specifically as a longitudinal study to allow me to explore students' passage through veterinary school in depth, and with the ability to investigate both continuity and change in students' stories. Within qualitative research in education, the tradition of longitudinal qualitative research is designed to chart change over time (Saldaña, 2003). Drawing from the field of theater, Saldaña (2003) asserts that longitudinal qualitative research works to identify a "through-line," which "describes, connects, and summarize the researcher's primary observations of participant change" (p. 151). As someone with a background in the arts and theater, this metaphor immediately and intrinsically made sense for me in my approach to my analysis of the qualitative data generated by my study. What—for each student, and then collectively—was their "through-line?" How do I make sense, in totality, of the stories that they told me over the years? In medical education, Balmer and Richards (2017) draw on Saldaña (2003) to suggest that some of the questions that can be pursued through this approach include, "what is different from one wave of data collection to another, what becomes more apparent over time, and what is the through-line of this participant's story" (p. 307).

My process in this research study is informed by the longitudinal qualitative research tradition, with some deviations for both practical/ethical and theoretical reasons. First, while Balmer and Richards (2017) highlight the centrality of each individual's "through line," I do not emphasize that aspect of the research in this book, even though I personally was cognizant of mapping that as I met with the students through the years. One of the key reasons that I de-emphasize individual stories throughout this book is to protect participant privacy. As a small study, I do not want a participant's privacy to be compromised by the ability of a reader to trace their story through the chronological development of the book. In addition, to protect participant anonymity in this study, I only refer to a participant's racial background or nationality if it is intrinsic to their story and experience. I am acutely aware that race, ethnicity, and nationality are critical aspects of my participants' journey through veterinary education, and particularly in Chapter 6 I share stories and experiences that are inevitably shaped by their positionality, as the tenor of participants' clinical year is largely influenced by their human interactions. As a researcher, my primary obligation in writing this book is to the participants who agreed to share their time and stories with me, and my commitment to protect them is paramount.

From a theoretical perspective, I am primarily interested in this research not simply as the accumulated stories of individuals, but instead to understand how their collective story (ies) illuminates how society's most respected teachers about animals are educated. Their story—created in this book through finding patterns in their multiple individual stories—is a part of creating societal change in human–animal relationships. Pelias (2015) suggests that human stories are at the core of what is valuable, unique, and ultimately indispensable about qualitative inquiry: the ability to foreground human story (ies) not solely for the mere proliferation of stories, but for a purpose: for social change and to tell "stories that matter" (p. 611). Thus, for me, the "through-lines" that matter are the collective ones, because it is in those patterns that the story of veterinary education emerges. I would expand upon Pelias' work and suggest that animal stories also matter, as has been extensively developed in the field of cognitive ethology, and which I discuss in greater detail in Chapter 7 (Allen & Bekoff, 1997; Bekoff, 2006, 2013; Bekoff & Jamieson, 1990; Bekoff & Pierce, 2010; Griffin, 1976).

As a researcher, I am inevitably influenced by my previous experience and education in the field of ethnography (Dolby, 2001) and my continuing interest in studying the cultures that humans create as a way of both understanding and making change. As an ethnographer, I am also drawn to studying human-created cycles of time, not because they are "natural" in any fundamental way, but because they are the way that we, as humans, think about our lives. For example, in my research in a school in Durban, South Africa in 1996, my research was contained within one academic school year—one cycle. In the research discussed in this book, I also identified a cycle within which to contain and frame the research: in this case, the cycle of an entire veterinary education, from matriculation to graduation. While I was unable, practically, to design and conduct an ethnographic study, my research perspective is still informed by this worldview and my previous experiences in the field.

Through this chapter I use the theoretical framework of "significant life experiences" to discuss how students' memories and experiences through their childhood, adolescence, and early adulthood formed the basis for motivation to enter the veterinary profession, creating contradictory dynamics in which students were socialized to both bond with and separate from animals. These moments and spaces of contradiction shape students' incoming beliefs, values, and attitudes toward animals as they enter veterinary school, forming an important context for their development of professional identity as a veterinarian.

Originally developed to study environmental activists (Chalwa, 1998; Payne, 1999; Tanner, 1980), "significant life experiences" (SLE) has been expanded in the past two decades and used to understand the values and worldviews of many social actors. While still predominantly employed in the field of environmental education (e.g., Howell & Allen, 2019), there are also limited examples in teacher education (e.g., Altan & Lane, 2018) and in research that works between environmental education and animal-oriented fields (Caplow & Thomsen, 2019). For example, Caplow and Thomsen (2019) use SLE to investigate how educators at three different animal related sites in North Carolina (Carolina Tiger Rescue, Duke Lemur Center, and the North Carolina Aquarium) use their animal experiences to influence/shape their career paths and foster engagement within a broader environmental education paradigm. Significant life experience research potentially encompasses both qualitative and quantitative approaches, though the research discussed in this book is solely qualitative. While relying on memory can potentially be an unreliable research approach, Chalwa (1998) argues that memory tends to be reliable when focused on the general arc of experience. Furthermore, how people make sense of their own memories and history is an important constructivist approach to social research.

In this research project, I see the framework of "significant life experiences" working in multiple ways. First, throughout the interviews, students were drawn to both identifying and discussing these moments before and then during their veterinary education that are pivotal for them. I found this framework to be particularly useful as I worked with the data from the first interviews, which is discussed in this chapter, because during those initial interviews I was asking students to remember the life experiences that led them to veterinary school.

As I continued with the interviews in subsequent years and read and re-read the data, I realized that "significant life experiences" could be a framework not only for the first year of interviews, but for the entire project. Much of students' experiences of veterinary school disappear into a blur. Students generally will have seven or eight courses each semester of the first two years of veterinary school. These early years are dominated by an enormous, crushing load of rote memorization. For example, students told me that in parasitology courses they were required to memorize more than 800 types of parasites. Even if "memorization" is not the way that a faculty member perceives the pedagogical objective of that course, that is how the students experience it, and thus defines their reality at the moment. The later clinical years are controlled by a punishing schedule that allows for few, if any, days off and little sleep. What is left in their memories of these days, weeks, and years is the essence of their feelings and that which is significant and meaningful to them: their "significant life experiences." This residual memory is consistent with the general arc of experience that Chalwa (1998) discusses, and it is thus an appropriate frame to use to think through the stories students tell. In this research, I attempt to capture these multiple registers: the experiences that were meaningful to them, their feelings about those experiences, and what those experiences mean for our society's relationship to animals.

There is also a third way I have come to understand the framework of "significant life experiences" for this project. As the years of the project ticked on, I began to realize that this research in and of itself was a "significant life experience" for the students who participated. As I entered year three and four of the interviews, students began to relax and share more openly, but they also began to see the interviews as an intrinsic part of their veterinary school experience. For many students, who were reluctant to access the limited counseling services available to them at the veterinary school, their yearly meeting with me provided a reflective moment that was unavailable elsewhere. Other students, who were actively meeting with the counseling office, would tell me about those meetings and what they discussed with the counselor.

Throughout the research, there were many intense, emotional moments. There were times when I left the room for a few minutes to allow a student to cry and gather her or his composure before continuing. There were also times, particularly in the later interviews, when I knew the students better and they trusted me more, where I sat with them through their tears (after of course, asking if they wanted privacy). These moments are discussed throughout the book. I know that for the students, these instances of concentrated emotional release were "significant life experiences" that were created and/or enabled by their participation in this research.

LOVING ANIMALS: MEMORIES AND SPACES OF CONNECTION

As I met students for the first time in 2015, they were overflowing with excitement mixed with trepidation. Some had taken a gap year between undergraduate and veterinary school and were experiencing the trials of being trapped in lecture halls for eight hours a day, after the relative freedom of the workplace. All of them knew that CMU delayed clinical experiences until the third year and were prepared for two years of tedium.

In those first interviews, I focused on getting to know the students as individuals, the variety of experiences they brought with them to their veterinary education, and their future plans and dreams. My general questions for the first interview included discussion of the student's background, history, and experience with animals, the career decision making process that led them to pursue veterinary medicine, anticipated challenges and rewards of a veterinary education, and their perspectives on animal welfare, animal rights, the human–animal bond, and working with humans. While these were the broad areas I wanted to explore, the interviews predictably meandered into different topics and moved in many directions, as I began to get to know the students whom I would follow through their veterinary education.

Entering this research project, I was familiar with research on medical students which indicated that empathy declined precipitously during medical school, a phenomenon that was referred to as the "hardening of the heart" (Newton et al., 2008). Would the same be true of veterinary students? Would they begin their veterinary education in 2015 full of empathy and love for animals, and end in 2019 bitter and detached?

I quickly discovered that the "hardening of the heart" model was too simplistic and linear to understand the patterns I began to see emerge in the first-year interviews.[1] Instead, the first-year interviews indicated that there were two distinct, contradictory—yet interrelated—pedagogical moments occurring from childhood through young adulthood. The participants in my study were simultaneously learning connection *and* disconnection from animals. As their personal experiences moved them toward animals, the larger society and culture intervened to instill a sense of separation and disconnection, reinforcing the differences between humans and animals, and minimizing and hiding the similarities.

This framework of "connection/disconnection" emerged for me primarily from my interviews with students. Marissa used the concept of "connection" in our first interview. As she discusses her relationship with animals she reflects,

It's almost like I had an understanding looking at an animal, without even knowing anything about it . . . like an energy almost I want to say. Like a connection between our energies, it's a little holistic. But I believe in energy and all that. So, definitely I think I am more energized around (animals), not even touching, but next to me.

For many of the students, the memories of animals they chose to share from earlier in their lives focused on their connections to animals. Heather tells a representative story of her relationship with her dogs,

Really strong memories I have. I would always play board games with my dogs. So I had this board game called Pretty Pretty Princess. It's this big board game with jewelry, and I remember that my mom had a job, so she would working, my dad would be working, so I would play with the dog. And I would move her piece for her and spin the dice and everything. We spent a lot of quality time together like that. Like she was a sibling, she really was a family member. My parents always treated the dogs like family members.

Like Heather, an animal provided companionship and friendship for Anna, who was shy and quiet as a child. She remembers,

I did have a guinea pig. She was my first pet. I think I was like five or six. And I remember just like the feeling of watching her crawl on the floor and everything, and I was just so in love, I was like this is so awesome. And then I would take her everywhere I went and that kind of thing. It was cool to have somebody there, something there, that I could love and everything, and I didn't have to talk. Because I was really shy when I was younger, and I didn't really like to talk to people. So when I was with my family, or my family friends, they always wanted to get me to talk. So it was nice just to have company without that pressure when I was younger.

For another student, Stephanie, emotional support came from horses and dogs,

> I really enjoy being out there with the horses. Maybe not so much a joyful memory but I always knew, if I am having a hard time in school, or I was stressed out in any way, they make it better. And this goes for dogs and horses both and probably other animals, but they listen and they look at you like they're understanding you, and you get it all off your chest, they don't give you any advice. They're like, you're right, nobody's telling you you're wrong, and they're really good therapy in that way.

Sadly, for Angela, her connection to her dog was her emotional anchor after her mother died when she was still in elementary school,

> It was just kind of, it's what got me through, through childhood was my connection with animals. My mother died when I was young, right after my seventh birthday. . . . We got him [our dog] about six months before my mom's accident that she passed away from. So he was kind of, he was how I got through all that. So a lot of my early animal memories I guess are associated with a lot of pain, but also all the comfort I got from him. That's why I could never imagine doing anything other than working with animals. That was a huge developmental plot in my life, was interacting and having my dog to get me through everything I experienced.

Finally, Laura, tells me a story that she did not remember herself, but had been passed down from her mother as "family lore" that explains her passion for helping animals,

> So I started watching Animal Planet and the story that my mom always tells is that everyone in our neighborhood would always come to me if there was like a stray or they needed food or something and I found a dead mouse apparently on the side of our house once when I was four, and I put it in a pencil case and brought it inside and tried to save him and bring him back to life. So I guess that was probably the moment that everyone says I realized it and I have just always been so interested in animals and helping them.

The feelings and emotions that the students are describing are often referred to in the literature as the "human–animal bond" referring to the innate, biological relationship between humans (an animal species) and animals (as defined by humans). The American Veterinary Medical Association (2021a) defines the human–animal bond as,

> The human-animal bond is a mutually beneficial and dynamic relationship between people and animals that is influenced by behaviors essential to the health and wellbeing of both. This includes, among other things, emotional, psychological, and physical interactions of people, animals, and the environment. The veterinarian's role in the human-animal bond is to maximize the potentials of this relationship between people and animals.

(n.p.)

While certainly it is possible to analyze these relationships through that paradigm, I think there is much that it missed through the lens of the human–animal bond. Most critically, the human–animal bond approach lacks a pedagogical perspective, and the acknowledgment that our human relationships to animals—while in part biological—are also learned. As I discussed in Chapter 2, the social and cultural context in which we are situated creates conditions in which we learn to love certain animals, eat some, use others for entertainment, and agree to sacrifice some to test cosmetics, pharmaceuticals, and medical devices (Herzog, 2010). The human–animal bond approach avoids these contradictions and nuances, focusing solely on the benefits of companion animals to humans. It is important to note that the centrality and importance of the human–animal bond is also contested within multiple fields, particularly psychology, anthrozoology, and in (so far) very limited research in veterinary medicine (Herzog, 2011; Rodriguez et al., 2020). For example, Herzog (2020) refers to what he has termed the "pet effect," which is the media and industry hyped idea that getting a pet will automatically make you a happier person. In addition, as the field of critical animal studies asserts, the use of the words "human" and "animal" (simultaneously joined and separated by a hyphen) serves to reify, instead of disrupt the socially constructed binary (Drew et al., 2019). Thus, while the human–animal bond is often used to analyze humans' relationships with animals, it is an inadequate frame to use for this book. However, as the human–animal bond is accepted as natural and commonsense in veterinary medicine, the term and the concept are present in my interviews with students.

A minority of students decided to enter veterinary medicine not to help animals, but to help people. For these students, the connection that they felt is to other people, not specifically to animals. This perspective was often present among students who planned to work with what (or, more accurately, "whom") the veterinary profession defines as "food" animals. Kiara, whose undergraduate background included experience with laboratory animals, describes it this way,

> I gained my interest in animals from my grandfather, he's a retired veterinarian. . . .
> I kind of have the mindset where I appreciate animals based on what they do for people as far as how they care for them, and companionship, but I also understand the aspect as far as why animals are used for research and how helpful they can be in order to progress the human race, so that's kind of my background animal-wise.

Michelle, who also followed the "food" animal track, explains the sense of connection that she believes that farmers feel both to their animals and to the humans they are helping, a value and perspective that she shares,

> I think, it definitely depends on the person, but for me I would say that people who don't see both sides, like they only have the companion animals, probably don't understand how or if people get attached to their cattle or something that's going to be slaughtered. But I think that as a farmer, someone who raises cattle, pigs, whatever, they have a different kind of connection. Like they still have respect for that animal, and they are always going to put its best interest at heart, but they know they are also helping feed America.

While not as common among students who planned to pursue careers in small animal/companion medicine, Alex expresses that his primary purpose and connection was to humans first and animals second,

> Right now I am kind of entering the veterinary profession in the mind that I am here to provide a service for people, and whatever good I do to the animals is more of a bonus to me.

LEARNING SEPARATION: THE CHALLENGE OF DISCONNECTION

What participants learned in childhood about animals was not always easy. As Christina discovered, one of the lessons was that animals are slaughtered for food,

> Especially with the goats, because they are very similar to dogs, they are very fuzzy, they're emotional, they like when you pet them. And we took them in showmanship classes, so we worked them a lot, we don't want them to misbehave or be scared of other people, so we spend a lot of time petting them, just playing with them like they are a dog, so you get kind of attached to them that way, but it's also hard, because at the end of 4H you sell them at an auction, because we showed market wethers. That was a little different, that was really hard, especially when I was younger, because it was hard to grasp the concept. It was like, this is my pet, I go out to see him, his name's Niblet. I pet him every day, but then one day I am going to sell him, and he's going to be sold to market, and someone's going to eat him. So that was hard.

Lin, who was raised in China, learned early to separate herself from animals who were raised for food, telling me,

> The only experience I have with farm animals is at my uncle's pig farm. And they raise the pigs. I tend not to show emotion with farm animals, but small animals, horses, like I just cannot handle it when they're in trouble, I want to help them.

The disconnections that participants discussed were not solely felt toward animals raised for food. Instead, their experiences early on reinforced the idea that humans are not only different from animals, but are superior, and that the feelings of connection that they have for animals can co-exist comfortably with the necessity of disconnection (Gillespie, 2018; Wilkie, 2010). For example, in the previous section Stephanie discussed her connections to both dogs and horses, particularly for the emotional support they provide. Yet later in the same interview, she clearly demonstrates that she learned to create limits and barriers to ensure that she did not become too attached,

> And don't get me wrong, I treat my animals like family, but by the same token, it's just a dog. Bella's got kicked by a mare before and knocked unconscious. And you know, we call the vet, he tells us what to give her, we give it to her, we're like if she doesn't wake up, or she broke a leg or anything like that, we have to make the decision is she going to live with it, or are we going to put her down. It's not "how much money can we spend to cast the leg" and do all this stuff.

For some of the students, the disconnection from animals began as they started to become interested in the scientific and medical aspects of animal bodies. Many students related experiences when they were young, and their family pet was either sick or dying animal. Suddenly they found their interest in what was happening from a medical perspective competing with their emotional bond to the animal. For example, Shanice tells me,

> I think I really decided to become a vet when my Rottweiler/Labrador, who we had for 13 years, she passed away because she had cancer in her liver and her spleen, and at that moment, I could see her kind of degrading, and her behaviors, and her eating and everything was just going downhill. And once we got her checked out and stuff, that was kind of interesting to me, the fact that I could kind of see the process, as well, towards the end.

Marissa had a similar experience when her elderly cat developed a chronic condition,

> I had a cat when I was younger, her name was Tira and I loved her to death. Older cats are predisposed to hyperthyroidism. I went to the vet with my mom, I wanted to understand. I was peppering the doctor with all of these questions. Although I was sad, I was more interested.

This sense of disconnection tended to grow stronger for students as they entered high school and college. Veterinary school admission requirements include hundreds of hours of hands-on experience in the field and almost always a letter of recommendation from a practicing veterinarian. Thus, students enter veterinary school with paid and volunteer experience at veterinary clinics and animal shelters, among other sites. These experiences reinforce the need to separate out emotions and feelings of connections from the medical puzzle that must be solved. Andrew, who worked at a veterinary hospital, relates how challenging and complicated these situations are,

> a lot of times, something will come in, and it's bad for the pet, but it's really interesting. So you feel bad for the pet, but then it's really interesting. But then I get, the joyful part comes if you are able to help the pet and relieve whatever is going on with it.

Heather, who worked in an animal research laboratory on her campus as an undergraduate, describes her experiences, and how she made sense of the invasive research that she did, along with her feelings of connection to the mice that she was responsible for taking care of,

> (my experience in the lab) definitely had a lot of negative times. So I will tell you first what we did. It's not what we did that bothered me. We would test dopamine receptor intake in rats, and see how that affected them, and then we would stress the animals, and see how that would affect them differently, like how the cells looked and how they functioned. So to do that, we would surgically implant something into them, so we could get drug specifically to the right part of the brain. Even the surgery didn't bother me. I did surgery, and I thought it was cool, and I liked it.

But what bothered me, was that sometimes the surgeries would go wrong. And uhm, well first of all, if a surgery went wrong and the animal passed away and we never got to use it, that would like really upset me. Because like I'm okay with using an animal for science, but if it died and it had no purpose, that's just the worst. And then sometimes they'd go through surgery, and uhm, we'd be using them, and the thing that we would use to infuse the drug into their brain, it would pop off their skull. And then obviously if you have exposed brain, you have to euthanize them. And then, again, not being able to use the animals after they have gone through that, is like really upsetting. That was definitely the worst part of research.

Heather went on to discuss the issue of naming the mice she worked with, and how that practice creates feelings of attachment. This is a theme that comes up frequently in my interviews with students and I will return to it again in the next chapter. An excerpt from our conversation is as follows,

Heather: Yeah, and it was hard because, when you do stuff, like to get the drug in you'd have to put, it's like tubing attached to a little almost like needles that you put in through the device to get the drug in. And to do that, you know, you hold them to put it in, and I loved holding them, and it was nice. It was hard to not get attached them.
Nadine: Did you get attached?
Heather: I did not. But it took everything not to get attached. I cared for them.
Nadine: Did you give them names?
Heather: No, yeah, that would be upsetting, yeah. I would name them if they were bad. If someone got bit, they would get a name, but otherwise, yeah, it would be too hard. Because I mean, we're studying the brain, so obviously at the end of the study we have to euthanize them, so it would be too hard to euthanize them if you got attached, and to name them. It was hard enough, with the little attachment I had.

A significant number of the students in my study considered entering the field of human medicine, but eventually, instead, chose to enter veterinary medicine. They often explained their decision by telling me that they were unable to cope with the blood and pain of fellow humans but were comfortable with animal pain and suffering. For example, Nicole tells me,

I grew up showing horses, but I never really thought about the idea of going to vet school. I was like, oh, I like animals, but not something like I want to work with them. But I always wanted to do something with medicine, so I thought, like I always really liked to go to the eye doctor, and I always loved that appointment, so I thought okay, well, maybe I want to be an eye doctor, and then I was like surgery, but then I can't handle human blood, that sort of freaks me out, makes me faint. But animal blood is fine. . . . I also think part of it is when an injury or something happens to a human, I almost feel like it's happening to me. So if you see someone break their leg, then I just kind of feel like, oh. But with the animals I don't really feel that way, I have a different mentality when dealing with animals than with people.

Laura tells how she feels queasy and uncomfortable with human blood, but is able to tolerate the blood of animals,

> So I always was interested in the medical aspect, and when I was little I used to watch all the TLC shows and ER and everything, so I quickly learned that human medicine was not for me. I can't do human blood and needles and stuff.

Finally, one of the students, Alex, intentionally created an experience for himself that would force him to confront the twin dynamics of connection and disconnection, by raising and then slaughtering animals, by himself,

> I know it sounds really silly, but . . . I had a friend who has forty acres and during my senior year of college I decided to go start a little poultry project. . . . So I raised like thirteen chicks, ten ducks, and then three turkeys. So I raised them until they were like adult animals, and it's from the livestock point of view. So I eventually had to slaughter the turkeys and some of the ducks. But I remember there was one instance where one of the ducklings had drowned accidentally in one of the tubs, and again that feeling of failure, failing to be a good caretaker came in and it kind of ate away at my ego and my confidence, like how is this going to reflect how good of a caretaker as a veterinarian I will be, you know. And uhm, I mean I guess that answers it. And then the slaughtering the animals that was pretty difficult, but it was kind of a good experience to, because it made me face myself as an omnivore.

More than other students, Alex was abundantly aware that to survive veterinary school he needed to confront himself as both a caretaker *and* an executioner. Unlike other students in the study, he fully understood the contradictions that are embedded in the veterinary profession, discussed them openly with me from the first interview, and had audible and persistent doubts about making it through the four years. Each year, when I contacted Alex for the next interview, I wondered whether he would respond—would he still be a veterinary student? Would he continue to the next year and stage?

As they enter veterinary school, many students feel a constant "splitting" between their feelings for animals and the larger social and cultural context, which teaches them to connect to certain animals and to disconnect from others. This splitting has also long been a component of veterinary medicine. As Jones (2003) discusses, the profession has historically viewed the value and position of an animal through its relationship to a human. For example, a "dog" in essence only exists as a being deserving of care and compassion if a human values that dog: a dog used for research in a lab becomes, in many ways, a different being entirely. Thus, while some students may expect that their veterinary school experience will help them to learn to negotiate these complicated dynamics, the reality is that for the most part, veterinary school simply avoids confronting this uncomfortable truth. Veterinary school also adds another layer of complexity to students' feelings, by (eventually) asking them to disconnect from all animals they meet through their profession. I focus here and throughout the book on the connections and disconnections that students learn through veterinary education, because both dynamics are ever-present in their education.

While most of the students in this study began veterinary school because of the connections they feel for (at least some) animals, by the time they graduate, animals have completely disappeared from the stories they tell about their everyday experiences. Thus, the story, and the through-line, that I expand on in the remainder of this book is one that slopes toward disconnection and eventually, the total disappearance of animals.

NOTE

1 Since the original publication of the "hardening of the heart" thesis in medical education, there has been considerable additional research leading to both enhanced nuance and critique. See Colliver et al. (2010), Roff (2015), and Teng et al. (2017).

4 Encountering Animal Bodies

At Central Midwest University (CMU), first and second year veterinary students spend most of their days sitting in lecture halls, taking basic medical science classes such as anatomy, histology, pathology, physiology, pharmacology, pathology, parasitology, and microbiology.[1] Mirroring the historic (though changing) medical school curricular approach, the overarching concept is that veterinary students learn normal medical science during their first year and then study disease processes the following year. The load is both tedious and demanding, with overwhelming amounts of memorization, incessant exams, a frenetic pace, and little rest.

During these initial years, and the summer between year one and two, many students have weekend jobs that involve animal care at veterinary clinics, animal shelters, farms, zoos, and other facilities. In contrast, students' experiences with animals through the first two years of their veterinary curriculum are limited. However, because wet labs are rare, those that do occur during these initial years in veterinary school take on a heightened importance as significant life experiences in students' professional socialization as veterinarians.

Hafferty (1991) notes that most studies of medical students focus on the clinical years of training, assuming that there is little socialization occurring during the basic medical science years. In contrast, his landmark study of medical students and their socialization to death concentrates solely on their first year, as they face death and dying through multiple experiences, including the dissection of a human cadaver during anatomy lab. Hafferty's insights reinforce my findings that the socialization of veterinary students begins early in their education, and that these beginning curricular experiences with live and dead animals are central experiences for students. As I discuss through the chapter, these encounters are professionally defining moments for students: they are seen and understood as rites of passages on their way to becoming veterinarians. For the students, the actual learning in those moments is not as important as the act of participating in the event and through that participation, becoming a veterinarian (see Chapter 2 for a related discussion in science education and Solot & Arluke, 1997).

Additionally, for many students these moments brought up disturbing and emotional responses which are powerful, *self*-defining experiences, but are never actually discussed in their classes. This sublimation of emotion, of powerful feelings, and of the contradictions inherent in the veterinary profession are also accepted—at this early point in the process—as necessary components of their education and thus their beginning socialization into the profession. While medical education has changed significantly in recent decades, the reality of the veterinary students in my research echoes the experience of medical students in Arluke and Hafferty's (1996) study of "dog lab" (a terminal medical procedure). While dog labs have been eliminated in

DOI: 10.1201/9781003269984-4

medical schools in the United States, Arluke and Hafferty (1996) write about the discomfort that medical students felt about dog lab in years past,

> Other tasks [e.g., dog lab] may be uncomfortable for students to do because they are experienced as morally tainted, provoking students to question the propriety of their acts. They are, after all, being trained to reduce or eliminate suffering, promote health, and compassionately care for the sick, but are called upon at various times in their education to do things that question these goals and challenge their emerging professional identities.

(pp. 202–203)

In the balance of this chapter, I first provide an overview of the veterinary curriculum and the tracking system. While students do not formally choose a track until later in their education, the track they are interested in at the beginning of their veterinary education creates the scaffolding in which they see and understand themselves, their classmates, their veterinary education, and the profession. As the delineations and divisions around track are fundamental to every aspect of veterinary education, this background is necessary to appreciate how students make sense of the "animal encounters" I explore in the remainder of the chapter. In the following sections, I discuss students' experiences with dogs, pigs, and chickens, as these are the primary animals that students interacted with during their first two years of veterinary education as part of the formal curriculum, and they were the stories that students most often discussed in depth during our interviews.

VETERINARY CURRICULUM, TRACKING, AND PROFESSIONAL SOCIALIZATION: AN OVERVIEW

Veterinary curricula across the 54 veterinary colleges that make up the American Association of Veterinary Medical Colleges are similar, conforming to a set of standards for accreditation purposes. Yet, they are not identical: their approach to curriculum and pedagogy varies and often reflects the historical strengths of the faculty and the needs and priorities of the geographic area. Despite these differences in emphasis, most veterinary colleges operate through a system of "tracks" which is a key self-organizing mechanism that contributes to both reflecting and producing the current veterinary profession. Tracks coincide with specialty areas. In that aspect, tracks educate veterinarians to provide appropriate medical care to the species of animals that they plan to specialize in and treat. Thus, at its simplest level, the system of tracks functions to organize animals within the veterinary curriculum. But within the context of veterinary education, tracks also take on critical meanings and organizational principle for *humans*, serving as a way for students to understand their own identities, emotions, feelings, and those of their classmates. In this way, tracks become more than administrative mechanisms, but perform a fundamental pedagogical function that shapes the perspectives of veterinary students, and in turn, the entire profession.

The most enduring and clear division, or track, within veterinary medicine and thus the veterinary curriculum is between "small" and "large" animal. And indeed,

CMU's teaching hospital, like the majority of veterinary teaching hospitals, include those descriptions in their official names: there is a "large" animal hospital and a "small" animal hospital. In broad sweeps, "small" animal tracks focus on animals who humans see as companions, while large animal tracks are centered on the animals who humans raise and slaughter for food, what the veterinary profession refers to as "production" or "food" animals. Thus, the monikers "small" and "large" are somewhat misleading adjectives, because they do not correspond clearly to the physical size of the animal. As Vermilya (2012) discusses in her extensive research on tracking in the veterinary profession, there are multiple cracks and fissures in this system. For example, a St. Bernard is physically larger than a chicken. Yet, the St. Bernard belongs at the small animal hospital and the chicken at the large animal hospital. A chicken is obviously a small animal, though it is considered a "large" animal for veterinary medical purposes. Vermilya (2012) argues that the animals who exist at the "border" of these categories are the ones who reveal the socially constructed nature of tracking and divisions in veterinary medicine. She particularly discusses horses, who though clearly not "small" animals, are often companions, and thus sometimes included as supplements to small animal medicine veterinary medicine (though for practical reasons, cannot generally be treated at small animal hospitals). Vermilya's research into the socially constructed status of horses in the veterinary profession occurred more than a decade ago, as the United States moved to eliminate horse slaughter, raising multiple ethical concerns that reverberated through the veterinary profession.

At the time of this study, CMU offered students multiple different tracks of specialization: small animal, equine, companion animals (which combines small animal and equine), large animal (which combines "food" animal and equine), mixed (a combination of small and large), or non-practice track, for students who plan a research-focused career, and require less clinical experience. The number and names of the tracks do vary across veterinary colleges, reflecting faculty research and teaching focus. For example, at the veterinary college studied by Vermilya (2012), students simply chose between "large" and "small" animal tracks.[2] At CMU, the contested and central status of horses is evident in this division of tracks, as they are positioned in both the "companion" and "large" track, in addition to having a track in which they are the sole focus. While not evident in the tracks available to CMU students as they entered in the fall of 2015, pigs also emerged as a "border" category in my research as the number of pigs who were admitted to the large animal hospital, but with owners—including several local farm animal sanctuaries—who expected the pigs to be treated as companions, began to trouble commonsense categories and what is considered fundamental veterinary knowledge about pigs.

Even as they entered veterinary school, most of the students in this study were already aware of the deep divisions in worldview and perspective that existed between students who specialized in "small" vs. "large" animals. As experience in the veterinary profession and a letter of recommendation from a practicing veterinarian is generally required for admission to veterinary college, it is not surprising that students are knowledgeable about how the profession is organized. Yet the power and intensity of their feelings and emotions was often surprising. Stephanie, who was from a family involved in the horse racetrack industry and planned to follow the equine track, struggled throughout her entire veterinary education with what she termed the "small animal mentality." Her awareness of and judgement toward the small animal side of veterinary medicine was clear even in the first interview:

> **Stephanie:** I'm really bad with, I feel like I'm really bad, very intolerant, with the small animal mentality.
> **Nadine:** How would you define the small animal mentality?
> **Stephanie:** That is to me, it's the people that, I hate being this judgmental, it's the people that treat their animals like family. My boyfriend's family has a dog . . . She rolled over and hit her paw on the entertainment center. She, to me, it was like, she had a stinger, there was nothing in her paw, she was licking at it, but I mean, she could walk on it, but she just gave them the puppy dog eyes, and they literally could not eat, because Maggie[3] was in pain. I'm very blunt when I talk, and in certain situations, I feel like if I was in a room with people who kind of acted that way, or really put their animal on a hierarchy, (big sigh), I just have a really hard time with it.

Stephanie continues to discuss her perspectives on how horses, despite being large animals, are often treated through what she termed the "small animal" lens,

> **Stephanie:** I mean, I feel bad saying that, but I really have a hard time accepting that people are calling horses companion animals now.
> **Nadine:** The vet school does because that's a track.
> **Stephanie:** Yes, in my mind, they're economic value. My family survives based off of how good we can progress the racehorse, and how well we can do with it, not how good it looks out on the yard as a lawn ornament. And it's very hard for me, for the people who keep pumping money into these animals, when they're not doing anything

Stephanie's critiques of the philosophical and affective approach of her colleagues, and of the companion track option in veterinary school, is indicative not solely of her own views but of the broader context of professional socialization. Sullivan et al. (2007) reflect on the importance of professional schools to the processes of both continuity and change within the profession,

> Professional schools are an institutional context in which the organized profession can exert control. They are perhaps the sole sites where the professions' standards of good work set the agenda for learning. Professional schools are not only where expert knowledge and judgment are communicated from advanced practitioner to beginner but are also the place where the profession puts its defining values and exemplars on display, where future practitioners can begin both to assume and to critically examine their future identities.

(pp. 3–4)

In Vermilya's (2012) research, she argues that the division within the veterinary field between (in broad sweeps) "small" and "large" animal produces a professional, collective identity that is "segmented" not unified. Sullivan et al. (2007) suggest that professional socialization is at its strongest in institutional settings where the profession asserts virtually complete control. The professionalization experience for veterinary students within this educational context is not total nor unified, but segmented. Students see, hear, and experience these differences among various segments of the veterinary profession as palpable and real, yet they are seldom, if ever, openly discussed. Instead, the segments exist and proceed in parallel lines, in silent agreement that the worldviews are fundamentally different and perhaps incompatible but necessary for the continuation of the profession. That silence, and the reality of needing to survive within those unspoken contradictions is one of the key defining values that students see and quietly absorb.

Students' experiences both before and during vet school beyond the classroom or the veterinary hospital are as important to their professional identity development as what happens in the classrooms, labs, and eventually teaching hospital at CMU. Students' reactions to the curricula experiences at CMU are always refracted through this larger context. The lines between the formal curriculum and what Blum (2016) refers to as the "wild" or real world are not bright and sharp lines, but instead very fluid. The "wild" is not simply what occurs beyond the door of the veterinary school or CMU's campus: there are times and places where the world of veterinary practice seeps into classes and curriculum. When and as this real world permeates the classroom, it is often accorded heightened respect, because it is the actual practice that will guide students in just a few years, when they graduate. The influence of segmented professional socialization in veterinary curriculum is strongest in the pig and chicken labs, with students who had no or limited experience with these animals. Yet, as evidenced in the students' reflections on these labs, the curriculum never stands alone: their acceptance (however reluctant) of what they saw and experienced in those labs is contingent on understanding these practices as "real world," and further solidified by their classmates' support and acceptance. Participation in these labs is a fundamental step in students' initiation into the profession: they begin to accept the "small" and "large" tracks as natural, pre-existing mindsets and approaches.

While not explicitly discussed with the veterinary students, at least in formal settings, tracks provide a powerful way that students' experience with the curriculum is organized as they progress through veterinary school. In the first two years, students take classes with all their classmates, as the tracks do not formally begin until the fifth semester (beginning of year three). Thus, the conflicts and tensions in the various perspectives are relatively intense through the first two years, and then diminish later, as students predominantly spend time with others who support and reinforce their worldview. If there is collective experience that veterinary students share, it is the first two years of basic science courses, and limited exposure to animals in a course in behavior, husbandry, and diagnostic techniques in domesticated animals. It is here, in these classes, that students have their initial encounters with animals as sanctioned and endorsed by the veterinary college.

LIVE DOGS, DEAD DOGS: THE FIRST ANIMAL
OF VETERINARY MEDICINE

The first animals that new veterinary students at CMU encounter are dogs, first alive and then later in the year, dead. The use of dogs in medical and veterinary education extends back to the earliest days of human and animal dissection in Europe in the 1600s, bolstered by Descartes' (1637/1960) assertion that animals were machines who did not feel pain (Hart et al., 2008). Thus, as domesticated animals who were generally complacent and cooperative with humans, dogs were subjected to what amounts to torture through invasive, live surgeries, ending in excruciating deaths. As human and veterinary medicine converged and then later divided (Heintzman, 2018; Mitsuda, 2017; Woods, 2017) dogs remain a constant presence in terminal surgeries in veterinary education well into the current century.

Though dogs are classified as "small animal" in terms of track and veterinary expertise, dogs are very much an aspect of all parts of the human world. Most students who planned to follow a large animal track were also bonded with dogs, and dogs are a constant companion to farmers and in agricultural settings. Indeed, my personal experience on my own institution's Institutional Animal Care and Use Committee (IACUC) included regular visits to Purdue animal care and farm facilities throughout the county. Often, when we got out of our university car at some remote farm facility, our group was greeted by a dog, who accompanied us throughout our tour. In this way, dogs transcend the tracks in veterinary medicine and symbolically represent the core of the veterinary profession: they are simply accepted as an animal that all veterinary students are (or will) bond with throughout their lives.

Dogs have such a central place in veterinary medicine that students without extensive experience with dogs or emotional attachment can feel that they simply do not fit in a veterinary college, and worry about their inability to understand dog owners. Alex, who was raised Muslim, explains his unique position,

> I volunteered at a cat shelter for three years, but I know next to nothing about dogs. It's kind of a cultural thing. I don't know for some reason dogs are considered unclean, so really I don't have much interaction with them. But that's not to say I share that view, but it kind of has an impact on my track. . . . We have lab dogs. I am really looking forward to that. Because as I have said, I have never been around dogs, I look forward to actually learning about them, and learning the bond. Because it will be kind of like my own little dog, and I have never had that experience. Maybe that way I will have more empathy towards people who own dogs, that feeling that is really important.

Like other veterinary colleges, CMU kept an on-campus colony of what was commonly referred to as "teaching dogs." While somewhat controversial, this colony of dogs was housed at the veterinary school and used for beginning veterinary students to learn basic procedures such as how to perform a wellness exam, draw blood, and place an IV and catheter. There are, of course, multiple ways to interpret the vernacular of "teaching dog." At one level, as Bone (2013) discusses in the context of preschool education the dog him or herself becomes a teacher and an educator. While this reality exists in the case of the "teaching dogs" it is not fully discussed or acknowledged either by the veterinary curriculum or the students. Instead, the dog is in many ways an object that students learn *on*, not from or with, as Pedersen (2011) maps in her analysis of how animals transition from sites of sentimentality to objects for learning as students progress through a formal education.[4] After their year of serving as a teaching dog, they are adopted out to new owners, often veterinary students.

As the students described to me, at the beginning of the academic year, first year students were placed in small groups, with each group being responsible for one dog: they were required to walk their dog, play with the dog, and clean the dog's kennel. The dog was also used in their first-year class on behavior, husbandry, and diagnostic techniques. During this year, students' encounters with the dogs are a break from the tedium of lectures and provide students' first opportunity to work with a real animal. Over the course of the year, students practice basic procedures on the dogs, who are generally tolerant and compliant. Anna explains her and her classmates' struggles to learn to place a catheter, using their teaching dog, Luna,

> Working with my lab dog Luna, we did lots of stuff with her, like drawing blood and placing catheters and stuff, and I feel especially placing catheters was a struggle for me. A lot of people in my group did it the first time, I was struggling to do it, I had never done it before. I got to see Luna all the time, but at the moment, I looked at her, and I was like, I'm sorry Luna, I'm screwing up your leg. But she looked back at me like she trusted me, where she was like, it's okay, you got this. And it made me think about it more that way, that I should stop poking this dog and torturing her, I should do it right, and looking at her, I could see that she trusted me, and it made me feel even more empowered to do a better job at what I was doing. Instead of just thinking I'm doing this on a cadaver or something, I'm doing this on an actual patient, and she trusted me to do it.

The students are aware that there is some controversy about the use of the teaching dogs at CMU. At times during my interviews, it appeared to me that the students had been directly instructed not to talk to people outside of the veterinary college about the dogs. For example, occasionally a participant would mention the teaching dogs, and then quickly retreat from the discussion. I would then tell the student that I had heard about the teaching dogs already, as other participants had discussed them. Students would generally seem relieved that they were not violating CMU's trust, and then feel free to discuss their experiences with the teaching dogs, and the university's concerns about the public perception of the dogs.[5] Multiple students told me that the dogs were specifically mentioned as a target for animal rights' protesters on campus. For example, Jennifer is quite explicit in drawing the connection between animal rights and the teaching dogs,

> During the animal rights that PETA [People for the Ethical Treatment of Animals] has every year, they warned us on campus, if you are on campus, around the teaching dog facility, make sure you are with somebody, because sometimes we have animal rights people who protest, and they may or may not be violent, and they had extra patrols. Even with the teaching dogs, they have this negative image of us being cruel to these dogs, and not treating them well . . . part of it is a negative connotation that people get,

they picture there's testing being done, there's twenty needles being stuck in this dog. They're in kennels, but they are taken out 3 or 4 times a day, and played with and loved, just like they are our pets. It's one of those things that, from the other side, you need to see what goes on day to day to make a fair judgement.

Yet, other students state bluntly that their classmates did not always take exemplary care of the dogs, and that perhaps there were reasons for concern. Heather's dog, Bella, was one who was very stressed from living in the kennel. From watching Bella and the other dogs, Heather begins to express some concerns about her classmates' level of empathy,

> Some of my classmates get frustrated that they have to walk the dog, and they have to clean the kennels. But you have to think, the dog is sitting in there, and they have to go so badly they go in their own kennel, that's pretty sad. So sometimes I get pretty frustrated with my classmates not really empathizing with the dogs as much as they should have.

The presence of the dogs also served as a point of cultural tension between students in the program. Heather tells me about an incident that happened during the year with another student. As she talks, I realized that this student was Alex, who was also a participant in this study,

> Actually there was one student who pushed my dog, and I went to the manager of the program, and I was really upset. They said they were going to talk to him, but nothing really happened. And for you to push a dog. He doesn't like dogs. Part of it, he's a Muslim, he explained before, because I did approach him and confronted him about it. He said he really doesn't like dogs, they are seen as dirty in his culture. But you can't push the dog, he pushed the dog down. And I was really upset about that.

The teaching dogs create moments of conflict and tension for first year students, as they are both required to form a relationship with the dog, and then to simultaneously use the dog as an object on which they are expected to learn (Pedersen, 2011). It is important to emphasize that the dogs, such as Luna, did not need a catheter inserted, or her blood drawn: there was no direct benefit to the dog. The students benefitted: they learned through performing these unnecessary procedures both how to handle a dog, but also the emotional lessons of the tensions in the veterinary profession: that animals are both patient and object. Similar to other points and moments of emotional conflict, these concerns are never directly discussed with students in their classrooms and labs, at least as students explained to me. Instead, they are trained to simply accept this reality and to continue with the task. Any feelings or moral quandaries are regarded as outside, not inside, the necessary professional socialization that is needed to become a veterinarian. The dog is, in most ways, the first animal of contemporary veterinary medicine, and thus it is critical that students implicitly learn during their first weeks of veterinary education how to bond with and simultaneously sever the bond with dogs. In the first year, students are generally accepting of this approach, yet as I discuss in future chapters, during the clinical years these concerns often becoming emotionally overwhelming.

DEAD DOGS: DISSECTION

Beginning veterinary students have a required course in dog dissection. Dead dogs, and dogs that are purposely killed for teaching purposes, have long been a part of both medical and veterinary education. Historically, medical students began their introduction to death and dead bodies through dissecting a human cadaver (Hafferty, 1991) and then progressing to what is known as "dog lab" (Arluke & Hafferty, 1996). Dog lab is referred to as a "terminal" surgery. Live dogs—sometimes purpose bred and sometimes from shelters—are deeply anesthetized and medical students perform procedures that allow them to observe the circulatory system. At the end of dog lab, the dog's heart is removed, and the dog is dead. After decades of protest, the use of live animals (dogs, pigs, and sometimes other animals) in medical training in the United States ended in 2016, when the University of Tennessee became the final institution to eliminate these practices.[6]

Considering the historical overlap between medical and veterinary education, terminal labs using dogs, pigs, sheep, and other animals have also been routinely used in veterinary training. While in medical training dogs are purely objects that are used to learn on and from to benefit human patients, in veterinary school, dogs are both objects *and* patients, potentially making the emotional toil and toll even more complicated for many students. CMU's veterinary college officially eliminated all small animal terminal surgeries the year that I started this research.[7] At the beginning of this research, I was unaware of this very recent policy change. When I mentioned the possibility of terminal surgeries (and explained what they are) to students, most were shocked and horrified, having never considered that such an activity might be part of veterinary education. One student, Brandon, was aware of CMU's decision, and very bitter about the lost learning opportunities, wondering how he was going to be able to learn surgical techniques without terminal labs.

While terminal surgeries and the emotional, ethical, and personal burden that comes with that initiation (Arluke & Hafferty, 1996) were not part of my participants' educational experience, dissection of dead dogs was a defining moment. In the development of veterinary schools in Europe in the 18th and 19th centuries, veterinary students routinely dissected horses, as they were the animal that veterinarians were most likely to need to provide care for as an individual animal. But in modern veterinary medicine, horse dissection is both unnecessary and logistically challenging, except for students entering equine specialties. All veterinary students at CMU, regardless of eventual track or career goals, participate in dog dissection—both frozen and fresh cadavers—through a required anatomy lab. Laura remembers,

> In our anatomy lab, the second day of class we walk in, and there's a room full of frozen, dead dogs on our tables. So I think that was something that was a little bit, oh my gosh, and of course it's a learning experience, but at the same time, you are seeing a room full of those dogs. Some were from shelters; you could tell that some had been attacked.

Many decades previously, dogs used for dissection, like dogs used for terminal labs, were often purpose-bred and then killed, to provide a uniform and controlled experience for student learning. By 2015, at CMU, the dog cadavers were generally donated by shelters after euthanizing, which as Laura explains, "They were received from shelters, feral animals that no one could control, those types of situations. That made it easier, knowing they weren't here just for our purpose."

Fresh cadavers, which were dissected later in the year, are more difficult, even for a student such as Stephanie, who had regularly attacked the "small animal" mentality of many of her classmates,

> One of the worst experiences I had was in anatomy, when we had the fresh cadavers (the dogs). There was only one starved dog, and we did not have that one. I don't know how I would have dealt with that. The worst, for me, it was the smell. I've done necropsies, but it's been out in the field. And you can always get a field direction where you don't smell it. And I think that's the closest I've ever been to getting sick with an animal. That was hard, just the smell, on top, of. You know, the frozen cadavers, they still look like a dog, they still are a dog. But they're hard, it's hard to pull the muscles apart. The fresh dogs, it's like, they just died, so take them apart. I've done foal necropsies before. And there is a reason there is such a thing as a small animal mentality, but I do think it's harder to do something that's considered man's best friend. That turned my stomach.

Despite how difficult and emotional the entry into anatomy lab and dog dissection was for students, it was never discussed in class with the professors. Faculty gave students directives for proper behavior, but beyond that, provided no emotional guidance or centering for students, Laura recalls,

> With our groups, it was just kind of discussing with our classmates, everyone felt kind of weird about it at the beginning. We got more comfortable with it over time, because we work with them so much. You just come in and you do what you got to do.

This mentality of simply doing what must be done, without serious reflection or thought about the moral and ethical concerns regarding the practice, echoes through much of medical and veterinary education. Arluke and Hafferty (1996) conclude that the medical students that they studied during "dog lab" learned that "it is acceptable, indeed even necessary, to suspend asking 'tough' questions in order to get on with their 'real' learning" (p. 223). The veterinary students in my study learned similar lessons from their experiences with dogs, lessons that would continue as they encounter pigs later in their first year of veterinary school.

SNARING SWINE[8]: LEARNING PIG BODIES

At CMU, like all veterinary schools, pigs are considered "food animals" and students are instructed in methods of handling and restraint that are common in production facilities and slaughterhouses. During a lab in one of their introductory courses on animal behavior, handling, and restraint, students are exposed to how the veterinary profession, in concert with agricultural and farm industries, interacts with pigs. The "pig lab" became a central, significant life experience for students in this study, as they try to make sense of this requirement, their feelings about it, and its place in their professional socialization. For many students in my study, this was one of the most difficult experiences of the first year, as they were required to learn how pigs are handled and restrained in production situations, using a snare. Pig snaring is a process based in violence, and one that often causes bruising and bleeding. Jennifer explains what the process entails, comparing it to her experience in that same week restraining a dog,

Like, if you go to the vet's office and your dog gets restrained, it looks like they are hugging the dog, and it's obviously not harmful to the dog, and it keeps them in place. But for pigs you can't really do that, because they're so massive, and they're so short to the ground. So instead, they use, it's called a swine snare, it's basically a snare, a metal loop. They'll stick it on the top jaw of the pig, and they just have to get it like behind the nose but in the middle of the top jaw, and then you lean back, and it tightens around the jaw. And then the pig's natural reaction is to pull against that, so it will tighten it even more, so it will pull back, and the pig will just stand there, and you'll run in, and you'll get a blood draw or something on them. But because it's a metal snare, it usually cuts up their mouth a little bit, not like to excessive amounts, but it will bleed a little bit, especially if they fight a lot.

Some students were disturbed that they and their classmates had to practice snaring the pigs repeatedly, even though the pigs were clearly being harmed. Anna comments,

with the pigs, I can see they have bruises on the back of their necks, some of my classmates were trying it multiple times, and I was like, is it really necessary? It's one swift motion, you don't need to practice it like eight times. That was frustrating to me. And I still to this day haven't done it, because I refuse to practice it. And I luckily haven't gotten pigs on the practical yet, so I haven't had to do it yet. And they said you can refuse to do it, but you lose like a fifth of your points. So in that situation, I'll do it if I have to, but I haven't had to yet.

Stephanie tells me that she was not personally affected by the way that the pigs were treated, but she could see that some of her classmates were,

The worst part for me, I had never learned to deal with them free, when we had to snare and stuff. And I was fine with it, the only problem was, Dr. X can't get us a pig per person. So we only had five or six pigs for the class, and when everyone has to practice snaring, they got bruised, and you know, I understood the process, and I was like, look, they're a food animal, they're being treated, they're being taken care of. It's not like they are being let loose after this to fend for themselves. So, I was okay with that, but a lot of my classmates could not handle the sight: they thought they were being abused or neglected or whatever. . . . It's not necessarily that I enjoy snaring them, because their hollers send chills up your spine, but that was different and it was good.

Listening to pigs squealing in terror, run, and being asked to harm an animal was challenging for many students, as was learning about common farm practices involving pigs. Marissa recalls her experience at the CMU swine farm,

We went to a swine farm. There's really not much space between a sow and her piglet. It's literally she does not have enough room to turn around. So I was like, why is it like that? And then a farmer was explaining to me that she will squish her piglets otherwise. I saw one get crushed, and it was put to sleep right there. And they're explaining to me how that happens, at least here in [state redacted]. They throw a piglet against the concrete because it's blunt force trauma, and it's the quickest way to relieve it. And I was like, wow, that's insane. Like I didn't know what else to say. Like I would never do that, never feel comfortable to do that.

I saw the piglet, they are so stinking cute, like choking . . . to see the farmer was emotionless, because it happens so often. That's an opinion, but then why else would it not bother you, it's so cute, and it's struggling to breathe. If I swap in a kitten or a dog that comes in and presents at an emergency hospital, there's arms flying, it's a different situation, when it happens to a food animal. I don't know if it's because, I'm trying to figure it out, I'm obviously frustrated talking about it, there are so many sows and they birth so many in one litter, like 18, so it's like one piglet out of 18. I'm trying to work it out. Just to see he was used to it, it bothered me, and I don't want to work with people like that.

On occasion, students expressed their concerns about the pigs to their instructors but were assured by the response that everything was normal, safe, and the way it was done in the industry. Anna discusses how she began to confront this reality of large animal practice through the pig labs,

Like with small animals, when you draw their blood, you have to go very slowly and calmly, and not hurt them, but they use the phrase of shooting a dart, when you do stuff (with large animals). And I'm always afraid I'm going to hurt them, but they are like, it's fine—not necessarily that they're being cruel to the animal, but it's not what I'm used to, because when you're in front of a small animal owner, you want to be as gentle as possible, because they'll be like, "you're hurting my baby." But with large animal it's like do whatever you have to do to get it done. So like with husbandry, that's mostly what I learned what I liked and didn't like. And with the large animals it was mostly about how they were going to go to market, and that's always what you have to keep in mind when treating them, and I don't necessarily like that.

For most of the students, the pig labs were part of confirming their veterinary path and track. From my conversations with the students, I surmised that the labs were not designed to try to convince students who were planning to focus on small animals to consider large animal medicine. Instead, the labs played a role in professional socialization, as students began to see the variety of roles veterinarians take up in society. Yet, this was not all that was happening for students through the experience of snaring pigs and visiting the pig farms. For students who were planning to track small animals, they were being socialized to accept the role and authority of their colleagues and to not question those practices, at least not too much. When students raised questions about what they saw, they were told it was "normal" to do this, and thus began to accept the authority and knowledge of their classmates and the industries. Thus, if asked later in their professional careers, they can honestly reply that yes, they have seen and participated in snaring a pig, and yes, the pig was harmed, but they were told and believe it is the best and only way. As Anna comments in the end, "I have tried to raise questions to them, but they reassure me that everything is okay. And I trust the instructors."

This trust that Anna places in her instructors to know what constitutes acceptable practice was widely shared among students. Many were shaken by the experience, but eventually accepted it as part of normal, everyday veterinary practice. Perhaps they were never going to work at a pig farm, or ever see another pig outside of a grocery store meat shelf, but through the experience they had learned to trust other veterinarians—their future colleagues—and to leave those decisions to them. In this way, they learned to accept the authority of the veterinary profession, grounding those decisions in what they could see (and were told) are real-world practices.

This real-world context is made clear to students, as the pig lab is not situated in a classroom in the veterinary college, but instead at a working, research farm, part of a sprawling agricultural operation owned by CMU.[9] The context, the visuals, and the smells of a pig farm add legitimacy to what the students are learning: they are immersed, if only for a few hours, in the world of pig operations, with its internal values and beliefs, which is reflected in its rhythms and practices. Snaring pigs, in this context, is normal, and accepted in the herd approach. Students might have reacted differently if they had been asked to snare one lone pig in a veterinary school classroom: in that context, it may have been easier to compare the pig to a dog and refuse to do it. But animals who are classified as food are treated differently than dogs, of course, and the sight of thousands of pigs housed together in barn after barn reinforces that difference. The acceptance of those differences, of course, does not begin in veterinary school, but through decades of earlier socialization, as discussed in Chapter 2. Michelle, who planned on (and eventually did) enter a swine medicine specialty, accepted that difference as simply normal,

> One of the differences between food animal and small animal is there is definitely less compassion I could say. . . . Walking through the farrowing pens, you see a dead piglet laying there, and they just scoop him up and put him on the ground or put him in this bucket. It's kind of hard because with a small animal you are so used to getting them cremated, or the family taking them home to bury them in the backyard. Little things like that that wouldn't affect the way I do my job, but little differences that make me a little bit sad, but you know you really can't do anything about it.

Brandon, who was planning on a career in small animal medicine, was also accepting of the differences, despite his knowledge and acceptance of the reality that dogs and pigs are cognitively and affectively similar. The following is a short excerpt from our conversation,

> **Brandon:** I have friends who work cattle and work pigs, and it's not ooey gooey love, it's this is a dollar sign in front of me. Some people definitely had shock when we had to snare a pig, a girl cried because they screamed when you do that, because obviously, getting gripped right here (motions to neck) would not feel that good, which, to me, it didn't really bother me, but some other people were definitely affected by it. Sure, it's an animal, but, if you have 1000 pigs to process and get through, you can't try and

do it necessarily, I mean, you have to be humane, but you know, you can't move a pig easily, so doing that is just what you have to do, I think.

Nadine: What if it had been snaring a dog, how would you have felt about that?

Brandon: Well, dogs, it's like, uhm, it definitely would have felt different.

Nadine: Why would it have felt different?

Brandon: I don't know, I just have a deeper relationship, I know dogs, and then the pig you know it's being used for food, even though pigs, research has shown that can have emotions, that they're smart, but for some reason I guess there's this disconnect even though they are both animals and they are both capable of similar kinds of processes, thought processes.

Only one student, Alex, indicated that he did not agree with the practices that they were being exposed to, and framed the experience within larger moral, ethical, and ultimately economic concerns. During the pig lab, Alex took the opportunity to have a private conversation with one of the PhD students who was instructing them on snaring techniques,

> There was one, a PhD student, she's really into pigs and stuff. I was like, I don't think I could ever be a pig vet, I don't know that I would be comfortable with all the practices. She was like, "yeah, they do a really good job of convincing you that what they are doing is right. Once you hear about the salaries you make, you basically drink their Kool-Aid, you do what they say".
>
> The pig is not able to do basic, natural behaviors. And they get locked in vices where they are just biting bars and stuff until their mouth gets bloody. And they have absolutely no stimulation, you know. And they get so big, like the way they have bred pigs generation after generation they are getting bigger, but they haven't changed the size of the crate. So they are even too big to fit in the crate. So I think the issue is, you could care less about the pig, but what does that say about yourself. Who are we as a people and as a society to be treating the animals we raise for food like that? So we should have a little more respect for the food that we eat.

Absent from the experience of the pig lab was any reflection on the possibility of a relationship, or a bond, with a farm animal such as a pig (Wilkie, 2010). Students felt compassion and empathy for the pigs, and many were opposed to the practices that they were exposed to during pig lab. Yet, the contradictory nature of the bond between farmers and animals bred for slaughter was never discussed: the students witnessed brutality, and for those who were not accustomed to these practices, it was shocking. For those students, pig lab did not necessary foster support for how pigs are treated, but perhaps a resignation that they needed to simply accept the reality of that aspect of veterinary medicine and focus on themselves and their own careers. In this way, pig lab underscored the segmented collective identity suggested by Vermilya (2015), allowing for the veterinary profession to continue to ignore its inherent conflicts.

However, what students missed during their experience in pig lab was an exploration of the real feelings and bond that many handlers and farmers have with their animals, including pigs. Following previous related research (e.g., Arluke & Hafferty, 1996), I suggest that the pedagogical objective of pig lab was to teach students a technique (here, pig snaring) so as to focus students' attention on a skill, the practice of that skill, and its place in the veterinary and agricultural world. The concentration on technique (and indeed, a grade linked to the successful performance of the technique) blunted and minimized any discussion of the moral, ethical, or emotional issues that may arise for students. But what was also lost was an opportunity to discuss the wider reality of the human–animal bond in the context of farm animals (Croney, 2014). As Wilkie (2010) discusses in-depth in her study of the relationship of handlers with animals who have been raised for slaughter, the everyday reality is often more complex than the simple and direct violence of pig snaring. Wilkie documents the intense and personal relationships that handlers develop with the animals that they see daily, befriending some, working hard to maintain emotional distance from others, and at times grieving over their deaths.[10] This complexity was evident to me on my farm inspections of pig farms through my term on my own university's IACUC: farm managers and handlers knew their animals, and often expressed emotions and feelings about and for them. Yet, veterinary students who participated in pig lab saw or heard nothing like this, for such a conversation would have cracked open a moral and ethical discussion, instead of one concentrated solely on techniques for handling and controlling pigs. My research here echoes that of Arluke (2004), who almost two decades ago suggested that veterinary and medical faculty avoid ethical discussions with students because of an "unarticulated fear of faculty that opening up and giving voice to these reservations might be dangerous to do—not quelling student concerns but exacerbating them—as a broader base of objection is inadvertently created" (p. 198).

FRIEND OR FOOD? CHICKEN LAB

In the final section of this chapter, I turn to a discussion of "chicken lab." Chicken lab is a terminal lab, which though prohibited at CMU for small animals, is still allowed for farm and large animals. During chicken lab, the focus on technique is again evident, but the moral and ethical questions raised for students are unavoidable, as by the end of the lab, the chicken is dead.

As the students explain it to me, the lab was part of their required coursework in animal husbandry, behavior, and diagnostic techniques. In the lab, they examined the chicken alive, learned a little about chicken behavior and had time to interact with their bird, then learned to kill the chicken through cervical dislocation and performed a necropsy on the warm, dead body.

Heather is particularly upset about this lab, as she explains what they were required to do, and that she exercised her option—available to all the students—to leave when they euthanized[11] the chickens,

> The chickens were a terrible lab. What they do is they brought us in, there's this room full of chickens. And each group of four grabs a chicken. And at first, you learn how to do physical restraint. So you are bonding with your bird. And then after 45 minutes of bonding with this bird, you euthanize it. I had to walk out of the room. Before it happened, I walked out of the room and sat down.

Unlike the pig lab, for which students could not present a clear curricular explanation for the activity, students were able to identify the justification that was extended to them for euthanizing the chicken. As multiple students explained to me, they were told that they all needed to be able to humanely euthanize a chicken through cervical dislocation, in case they were driving down the road and found an injured chicken who needed to be quickly euthanized. Heather continued,

> Even though I kept telling myself it's important for us to know how to do this. Because they said to us, you know, if you ever see a bird on the side of the road that needs to be euthanized. I know it's fast and everything. First of all, the idea that we were interacting personally with these birds first, and then euthanizing them. I know it's different for kids with farm backgrounds, but I felt like I was having this nice experience with this animal, and then I kill it, and it's all just for my education. I just feel like we didn't need to euthanize them. And I know they told us that the birds were sick or otherwise couldn't be used or whatever. But it just seemed like we were just killing these birds. We did a necropsy on them, but most people weren't paying attention or didn't care. So it just seems like these animals were needlessly euthanized, and that really sucks.

Marissa similarly explains how she feels that as a veterinarian she needs to be able to do this, and that the professor's explanation of needing to be able to euthanize a chicken found by the side of the road is legitimate,

> Even though I won't be practicing on that type of livestock, there might be a situation where I might have to. Our professor said, literally, she was driving one day, and she saw some sort of chicken on the side of the road in distress, and she pulled over, and she cervically dislocated, because she was educated on how to do it properly, in veterinary school. I was like, you never know what's going to happen.

Nicole was one of the students who stayed in the room but did not euthanize the chicken herself. She discussed her discomfort,

> The chickens were interesting, actually. They were fun to play with. I didn't know you could hypnotize chickens—dragging their head on the ground. That was cool. But also, we were supposed to kill our chickens after that. I did not volunteer to be the one from our group that killed our chicken. I stayed in there and watched them do it. They let people leave the room if you didn't want to see it. I thought what was really hard about that was a lot of people didn't break the neck on the first try or even the second try, so it took them three or four tries to break the neck. And that kind of made me cringe quite a bit.

Alex remembers that "The chicken lab was kind of sad, because we named the chicken, and then we had to kill it." Nicole similarly reflects how she bonded with her chicken and did not want the chicken to die,

> You kind of like bond with your chicken. You're like, I like my chicken, I don't want to kill my chicken. . . . We weren't with it that long, it wasn't that big of a deal. It's not like I wouldn't have killed it if they told me I had to, but I would have preferred not to do it.

For the few students with specific experience with poultry, the chicken lab was a chance to share their expertise and their emotional calm with their less experienced colleagues. Christina, who regularly spent her summers working in chicken barns full of millions of chickens, explains her experience of the lab,

> I know I'm still learning, but it was really cool to be able to teach the other people who had never dealt with a chicken, just how to hold it, how to be safe for you and the bird . . . teaching people different things, like you can hypnotize chickens. Being able to help someone with their first experience, and their being able to say, oh my gosh, this is kind of cool.
>
> I stayed there; I think I euthanized one chicken. Because I had done that before in my job and also, we butcher our own chickens at home. I've been around this a lot. There were the people who left who were like, I don't want to have any part of this, and some people were like, not excited, but they wanted to learn. And I feel I was just there to help them, and talk to them how to do it, and give them things, like, most people don't pull hard enough. . . . We had the three chickens in our group, so we just chose the three people who wanted to do it, and I kind of just helped them, and watched them do it. They all did a really good job *and I congratulated them, see, it's not that bad* (my emphasis).

As with the pig lab, there were no opportunities for students to talk with faculty about any emotional reactions they had about their interactions with the chickens, both alive and dead. Students who left the chicken lab and stayed in the hallway did talk, as several of them told me. Some of the students remembered that only about three students left, others remember up to six or seven. Heather recollects,

> There were like 4 or 5 other people out there during the euthanasia process. But we didn't really talk. As soon as I turned around and saw it, I started crying. So they were just trying to comfort me. We didn't really talk about what was bothering us, we were just like trying to talk about the weather and take our minds off of it. Now that I am thinking about it, one of the technicians who works with the classes was out there too, and she had made the comment that doing that lab really bothered her, and she didn't want to be in there, she didn't want to be a part of it. And she used to be a large animal technician, so she's more of the farm mind.

Heather feels that her emotions are valid because a technician with considerable large animal and farm experience, though not a veterinary student, had also left and refused to watch the euthanasia. In this case, Heather, has little to no opportunity to discuss the ethical and moral concerns that she has, so she instead she closely watches the attitudes, behaviors, and reactions of those around her who have real life experience.

Though on the opposite side of the spectrum (toward acceptance instead of rejection), Christina's "congratulation" to her classmates who successfully killed their chicken serves a similar function of validating feelings and emotions based on "real life" experiences: it assures them that their actions are fine and acceptable, both in the classroom and in the world outside. As I have discussed previously, veterinary students use real-world practices as a source of professional socialization, in equal measure to what is presented to them through the curriculum. Thus, Christina's gesture of support and congratulations is an important step for them in their professional identity development: they have successfully performed a technique that they believe is common in the veterinary world. But perhaps more importantly, Christina's comment that "it's not that bad" supports them in the process of beginning to bury their emotions and their moral and ethical qualms, as they now understand that is a step necessary to becoming a veterinarian.

Such an approach has a long history in veterinary medicine. Rollin (2019) reflects on his experience in the late 1970s beginning to fully study and understand the serious ethical issues surrounding animal pain and suffering in veterinary medicine. After witnessing a particularly horrific procedure in a student lab, Rollin asked the professor who had created the lab what the objective was, and reports that the professor responded, "it is to teach the students that they are in veterinary school now, and if they are soft, get the hell out early" (p. 397).

Despite the curricular focus on technique as a strategy for avoiding the moral and ethical issues involved in the chicken lab and any discussion in the classroom, students were aware that this lab was problematic, if not to themselves personally then to their classmates. Almost all of the students, whether they participated in the lab or not, brought up one of the most salient concerns of all: how and why were these chickens chosen? Every student I interviewed indicated that a rationale for the choice of these chickens had been presented at the beginning of the lab. Yet, during our conversations, students brought up multiple alternative rationales and sometimes contradictory explanations. I was told that the chickens were old, that they were sick, that they were research chickens that needed to be euthanized, and that they were simply randomly selected. Given the wide range of answers, what seemed to be important to the students is the faculty *did* provide a reason for killing these particular chickens. Even if did not make sense, even if their classmates believed something different, they clung to the short explanation that was provided. As Arluke and Hafferty (1996) argue in their analysis of medical students' reactions to dog lab, the explanation provided by the faculty gave the students "absolution": they were not responsible for the chickens' deaths, someone else was. While this provided little comfort for the few students who truly were disturbed by the day's events, for most, it was enough to know that there was a reason, and they could trust the faculty to make these decisions. While this trust erodes quite dramatically by the fourth year, students' early professional socialization is structured to compel them to believe in the faculty and the veterinary profession to make the correct decisions *for* them. This is evident in Andrew's practical and unemotional retelling of the experience. For him, and for some other students in this study, chicken lab was just another day at school, "We learned how to do a short physical on a chicken, how to hypnotize the chicken, that was fun. Then we did cervical dislocation in order to kill it, and then we did a necropsy on it."

CONCLUSION: TOWARD SILENCE AND ANIMAL BODIES

First and second year veterinary students at CMU have very limited opportunities to work with real animals—alive or dead—through the formal curriculum.

As a result, the experiences that they do have become significant life experiences that are formative moments of professional socialization. Through these experiences, students are not, in any large measure, learning material, techniques, or approaches that are important to veterinary medicine: instead, they are learning what it means to be a veterinarian, and the attitudes, behaviors, demeanor, and beliefs of the profession. As I have discussed throughout this chapter, one of the major learnings is that animals are objects to be learned on, not with. For example, despite the students' confusion about how and why the chickens were selected to be euthanized through cervical dislocation in the chicken lab, some clearly understood that the animal was being used as an object and had concerns about this practice. Anna, one of the students who left the room during the cervical dislocation, tells me in detail what she saw and heard,

> So when the guy did the demonstration in front of us, he cervically dislocated it and then threw it in a bucket. It was like still moving around in there. . . . And while I was outside the room, I started hearing chickens hit the bucket and hearing flopping and stuff and even that was hard to hear, I was like, oh, those poor chickens.

Others, though equally cognizant that animals were being treated as objects, accepted it as a common veterinary practice.

Through these labs, students were socialized to accept the norms and practices of the entire veterinary profession, including tracks outside of their personal experience and perhaps comfort zone. Thus, for students following small animal/companion tracks, the forced exercise in pig snaring was designed, at one level, to familiarize veterinary students with industry practices in food production. Indeed, while the students in this study did not participate in a mandatory visit to a slaughterhouse, that is an accepted activity at some veterinary colleges (Pedersen, 2013). Embedded in this curricula approach are also deep aspects of socialization: that students should not only be familiar with what happens with "food" animals, but through accepting the accumulated knowledge and history of the veterinary profession, should accept and trust that these practices are humane and the best. For students who have worked their entire lives to be able to enter the veterinary profession, despite their misgivings, they feel there is little choice but to simply move on to the next class, exam, lab, or clinical experience.

As there is no classroom-based discussion of students' feelings of sadness, anger, or discomfort, they also learn that this is the norm in veterinary medicine: to simply accept the practices that you are taught. As Gage and Gage (1993) suggest, this is the mentality of a trade school, where students work on cars, trucks, engines, and other inanimate objects. But veterinary students are learning to treat animals, not fix cars: they are constantly encountering sentient beings, despite the sublimation of that truth. Even if students do not agree with the "trade school" mentality, and some do not, they accept it as the implicit norm of the profession, both within and outside of the university. Students' emotions and reactions to chicken lab, their relationship with their chicken, their own feelings, and their observations about their classmates' reactions are all part of a complex initiation rite on their way to becoming veterinarians.

As students finish their first two years of veterinary education, they begin to understand more of what is expected of them as human beings who are in the process of becoming veterinarians. The second year ends in a flurry of exams, amid the anticipation of their "last summer" before the non-stop intensity of third (classroom and clinical) and fourth (clinical) years begins in the fall.

NOTES

1   Over the past decades, veterinary colleges have responded to student desires for clinical experiences earlier in their degree programs, and many have started to incorporate hospital-based rotations and early experiences into their first- and second-year programs. While more recently CMU has moved in that direction, the class of 2019 entered a veterinary college that largely expected them to spend their first two years in the classroom.

2   More recently, some veterinary colleges are beginning to move away from the track approach, instead focusing on a system of specialties and electives.

3   The names of animals throughout the book are also pseudonyms, to protect privacy.

4   See previous discussion in Chapter 2 for context and background.

5   I should note that CMU's policy toward public discussion of the teaching dogs seems to have shifted since the time of this research study. While writing this book in 2021, I noticed that (what I assumed to be) the teaching dog program prominently featured in CMU's social media, rebranded, and promoted as a positive feature of the veterinary education program. It is possible that some of the concerns expressed by the students in this chapter have been addressed, now that the program has a public face and media presence, but I have no way to know or confirm that this is true.

6   It is important to note that these practices continue in surgical training programs and are widespread in research. Pigs and sheep are particularly used extensively in medical device research and this type of terminal animal research is generally required before testing in humans.

7   The American Association of Veterinary Medical Colleges encourages alternative to live animal use in veterinary medical education but does not prohibit most practices as long as they are allowed by the institution's IACUC and follow all required federal guidelines. The policy is set to be revisited/updated again in 2023.

8   The industry refers to any animal used for pork and other food production as "swine" and the term "pig" is reserved for babies only.

9   It is important to add that practices at CMU, similar to all research universities, differ depending on whether, for example, the pig is located on the main campus in a research lab or on the CMU farm. At the research lab, CMU must follow all federal and university regulations regarding animal care and use. At the farm, "Farm SOP" (standard operating procedure) governs practices and thus allows for much greater latitude in what is permissible.

10 See also Peden et al. (2020) for related research that underscores that pig farmers do have an understanding of pigs' sentience, and thus capacity to suffer.

11 In this case, it is reasonable to question the use of the word "euthanize." Euthanasia is a painless death, and in veterinary medicine, is most commonly used in small animal medicine. Cervical dislocation, the technique that the students were taught that day, if performed correctly, is believed to be a painless humane death. However, as is evident through the student descriptions of this lab, students were learning how to do this technique, and thus it is questionable as to whether it is painless for the chicken. Beyond that clear concern, scientific evidence in the case of animals used for food is often partial, incomplete, and used to support industry objectives. See Blackwell and Rollin (2008).

5 Stepping Out
Learning in the Wild

After the second year of veterinary school concludes in May, students have what is referred to as their "last summer." At CMU, when the third-year finishes, students have a break of one weekend and then begin a series of 17 three-week rotations, culminating in graduation. While these rotations follow the multiple tracks discussed in previous chapters, students are also widely exposed to many aspects of patient care and veterinary medicine. For example, all students are required to enroll in rotations focused on small and large animal medicine and surgery, anesthesia, diagnostic imaging, necropsy, clinical pathology, and microbiology. Students then choose from dozens of electives that include all the specialty areas in the small and large teaching hospital, multiple community practice sites focused on different species, and opportunities in production medicine for students following food animal tracks. While the veterinary college encourages students to use one of these rotations for a vacation, students sometimes use it for an additional professional experience.[1]

For many students, the summer after the second year of veterinary school is both the last summer of veterinary school and the final summer they will experience as a student before they begin their veterinary careers. For some, this is a final opportunity to relax before the start of the second half of veterinary school and the beginning of their professional lives. A few of the participants returned for one more time to regular summer jobs, such as lifeguarding. One of the students in this study, who felt that she needed to work on her communication skills, took a job working at the counter of a local coffee shop serving customers. Many of the students find or return to positions in veterinary practices, animal shelters, and other animal related businesses and organizations. A few remain on campus and work in the veterinary hospital. Students in this study who were funded by the United States Department of Agriculture completed a series of internships.

For all the students, this summer was a significant turning point in their veterinary journey. They returned to veterinary school as third years, ready to start their electives, junior surgery, and the process of arranging their required externship and optional off-campus rotations for the fourth year. The required externship is designed to give students experience in a veterinary practice in their proposed specialty area, while the optional off-campus rotations are designed to accommodate special interests or training not available at CMU. The fourth year of the veterinary curriculum was carefully orchestrated and planned to accommodate each student's career path. Students had wide latitude to arrange externships and off-campus experiences at veterinary practices, teaching hospitals, wildlife centers, and other sites around the world. In some cases, students returned to sites that they had visited on earlier study abroad trips in veterinary school. CMU's administrative offices also work with alumni worldwide in a vast network that invites fourth years for a three-week

DOI: 10.1201/9781003269984-5

rotation, often providing short-term housing. Students who wanted unique experiences to be able to potentially follow career paths in zoos, aquariums, marine centers, and animal welfare organizations were able to craft rotations that fit into their fourth year. In addition, third year students began to prepare for the national veterinary board exams (North American Veterinary Licensing Examination), which students typically take during the fall of their fourth year.

Because of the consolidated nature of the third and fourth year of veterinary school, students often do not see much separation between the two (and indeed, there was no separation, except for a weekend). The boundary between the third and the fourth years also dissolved during my interviews, with students often having difficulty remembering when exactly a particular experience occurred in the academic calendar. Because of the intense focus on fourth year preparation during the third year of veterinary school, and the lack of a break between the two years, this chapter combines the third year and the beginning of the fourth year into a chapter that focuses on students' early clinical experiences.

The schedule changes of the third and fourth years also dictated the timing of the fourth and fifth interviews in this research study. The first three interviews (2015, 2016, and 2017) happened in the late summer or early fall, just as the semester started. If I had continued with this schedule, the fourth interview (2018) would have occurred in August or September, which was, by that time, well into the fourth year. Additionally, because of externships and off-campus rotations, students were not as reliably available on campus anymore. If I intended to continue with face-to-face interviews, I needed to work around their increasingly demanding schedules.

As a result, I made several modifications to the practices I had used earlier in the study. First, I adjusted the timing, so that I met with students toward the beginning of their clinical rotations in 2018, and then again right before graduation in 2019. CMU's veterinary school had requested that I not interview students during the first three-week rotation (a mandatory, on-campus rotation at the teaching hospital), and I also felt it best that I allow students time to adjust before interviewing. Most of the students' fourth interviews were held during their second or third rotation (primarily early summer of 2018) except for a few who were away from campus and were thus interviewed when they got back. The 2018 and 2019 interviews were held in a conference room adjacent to the teaching hospital, so that students could quickly return to their duties and responsibilities and were close by in case they were needed in an emergency. Previous years the interviews had occurred in multiple classroom and conference spaces around campus. This arrangement was primarily for students' psychological comfort. The research study was approved by the veterinary college, and I gave students a letter from me that they could present to their immediate supervisor, requesting that they be excused for 90 minutes to meet with me. From an administrative perspective, this was a minor request, and there seemed to be little to no concern with students being absent for a mere 90 minutes. Yet, during the interviews at the beginning of the clinical rotations, students were so nervous and anxious that they felt they could not miss one moment of their rotation, or they would risk failure. Most of the students scheduled the interviews for times they knew they would not be required to be present in the hospital, or on-call. They sacrificed sleep, food, and showers to meet with me.[2]

As I held the first interviews in the early summer of 2018, I noticed how students had changed. They seemed older, often wearing their white coats, and were tired. Most were talking to me after a long day at the hospital that often started at 6 a.m. Many would complete their interview with me and return to the hospital for paperwork. Others would go home for a quick dinner and shower and then go back to check on patients. Students also noticed and reflected on the difference. For example, Jennifer told me,

> Third year, the second-semester finals was rough. I honestly don't really remember much of first semester. It feels like forever ago. . . . It was just a big adjustment to fourth-year hospital versus classroom life is very different. I'm still working on getting better at time management because a lot of our clinicians expect us to be juggling five things [laughter] at the same time, so I'm getting there.
>
> I did like junior [third year] surgery, actually quite a lot. None of us knew what we were doing, and we were all very nervous, so they had to have a clinician stay in with us the whole time and walk us through everything. A lot of those times we wouldn't even finish our surgeries until like 6 or 7 o'clock at night. And then we had to wait until the patient recovered, and then we had to come back and do late night checks, and so there's usually like a 5, 8, and 11 o'clock check. So there was lots of nights that I spent really late in the hospital.

I attempted to schedule interviews with students while they were on rotations that were less time-intensive, and not medicine or surgery rotations. But that was not always possible.

More than anything, it was clear that students' mindset had changed in the past year. They had "stepped out" of their predominantly student role, into a more liminal space (Turner, 1969) and one that was firmly located in the wilds—in the real world (Blum, 2016). Of course, they were still students completing required clinical rotations for graduation and licensing, but their frames of reference were bigger and wider: now, CMU was one node in a much larger structure. In this chapter, I examine students' significant life experiences through the lens of liminality. Building on the earlier scholarship of Van Gennep (1908/1960), Turner (1969) extended the concept of liminality to describe individuals or groups who are transitioning between stages. Liminality has been used a framework of analysis for many contexts that are equivalent to veterinary education, for example, in studies of doctoral students, academics throughout the world who do not have PhDs, and medical students (Breier et al., 2020; Gordon et al., 2020).

As students began to explore this new perspective on themselves, the central questions of my interviews with them took on new meaning. In every interview, I had structured the questions around three overarching themes: what they had learned about themselves and the veterinary profession, what they had learned about animals and their relationships with animals, and what they had learned about their relationships with humans. In this chapter, I use those questions as the structure for exploration and discussion, as my participants begin the first real steps on their professional journey. Because the focus of this chapter is on how students "step out" into the wilds of the real world, I also use some of the students' veterinary experiences from the previous summers, as those experiences are formative in their understanding of the profession and their place in it.

In the first section, I center the significant life experiences that informed students' professional socialization: what they are learning about what it means to be a veterinarian, how they consciously (and sometimes unconsciously) absorb the norms and values of the profession, and how they begin to negotiate their emotions and ethical concerns. I then extend this conversation into students' early experiences with animals through their junior year and into their first rotations. Students' connections with animals at this juncture are both powerful and poignant, as they wrestle with the hidden and largely silenced ethical issues that they confront daily. The final section of the chapter focuses on their relationships with humans. While barely mentioned in my earlier interviews with the students, at this point in their veterinary journey, relationships with other humans—as supervisors, teachers, clients and owners—become salient to their stories of veterinary school. The students begin to explore both their own relationships with other humans they encounter and become more observant of the human–animal connections that they see every day.

I AM A DOCTOR? FIRST STEPS

At CMU, veterinary students' formal transition from student to doctor begins with the white coat ceremony which was held toward the end of their third year, immediately before third year final exams and the beginning of fourth year clinical rotations. Medical schools have held white coat ceremonies for incoming medical students for over three decades (Goldberg, 2008; Vinson, 2018). Typically, during medical school orientation, students recite the Hippocratic Oath, receive their white coats, and are welcomed into the medical profession as they begin their classes. Veterinary schools soon adopted the practice for their students, though they differ as to whether they have the white coat ceremony at matriculation or before clinical rotations begin, as CMU did in 2018. Students recite the veterinary oath, don their white coats, and listen to speakers applauding their success so far, and supporting them on the next steps toward becoming a licensed veterinarian.

The coat itself seemed to hold only minimal meaning for the veterinary students in this study, in opposition to the multiple ways that medical students used the coats as symbols of knowledge and status (Vinson, 2018). Unlike medical students, veterinary students in my study only wore their white coats while in the veterinary teaching hospital: they were, of course, not worn in many rotations and contexts off campus where a thin white coat is decidedly impractical. Thus, while medical students in Vinson's study (2018) donned the coat daily for four years, veterinary students in my study wore it intermittently, and only for one year. I discuss the oath in more detail in Chapter 6, as I specifically asked students about its meaning to them in the final interviews before they graduated. None of the students mentioned it in the interviews discussed in this chapter.

Nevertheless, the white coat ceremony marked a crucial turning point for students: they begin to see and position themselves outside of the role of student and inside the veterinary profession as a beginning doctor, thus beginning a phase of transitional liminality (Bamber et al., 2017). The real-world context of clinical blocks allowed for students to relax and learn new techniques without the stress of the veterinary hospital and to "forget" some of the strict protocols of veterinary school. Goldberg (2008) discusses that for medical students, the white coat ceremony, occurring at the beginning of their medical education, is a moment where students are asked to disregard their humanity and don the (figurative and literal) white coat of the profession. While certainly this is one current that exists for the veterinary students in my study at the beginning of their clinical rotations, what is more remarkable and notable is that this is a moment in their education in which their emotions for animals and for working *with* and *for* (instead of *on*) animals are renewed, recalling my first interviews as they entered veterinary school.

Alison explains her pure joy at learning to intubate a possum at a zoo through a community-focused rotation,

> I learned how to intubate a possum, which was kind of cool. Their mouths are huge [laughter]. One thing that's different that I think is kind of interesting about their mouths is that—this is a really simple thing—but you think with dogs and cats and other animals, they can only open up so much, like maybe about—you know, that much. But then with a possum, you can go all the way up and all the way through the back. You could see everything. Their mouths open so wide [laughter]. But then that makes it easy to see a trachea and all, so that works out.

Stephanie similarly felt freed by practicing in a real-world context, instead of the rarified and precise world of the veterinary hospital,

> That's one reason that I appreciate Equine Community Practice because it's a lot more real-world. Here [in the hospital], we draw back medication, and then we have to get a new needle because you've poked the needle into the bottle once. I did that first day on ECP. She goes, "No. No. No. We're not in the hospital. Just do it."

For some students, this means beginning to push back more forcefully against the suggestions made by the veterinary college. For example, CMU strongly recommends that students not use their allocated vacation for additional professional experience. However, that is exactly what Christina did, as she explains to me,

> I was just like coming off RAVs [Rural Area Veterinary Services]. And I'm going on RAVs again, actually next block [rotation] on my vacation. . . . Which, I've been advised [against] many a time. I don't want to do that and all that stuff. But that's exactly what I want to do and sign out.

For Christina, her time at the Rural Area Veterinary Services (RAVS), a mobile veterinary clinic that serves low-income, rural populations in the West and Southwest, often on Native American reservations, was liberating, allowing her freedom and decision making that was unavailable within the confines of the veterinary hospital, with its strict hierarchies. Similarly, Christina was energized by her rotation on a local mobile spay and neuter clinic sponsored by the veterinary college. She tells me about a typical conversation between herself and the veterinary technicians who staff the mobile clinic,

"Oh, hey Doc, what do you think about Fluffy?" And so then we have to assess and decide if we want to give them a full reversal, a half reversal [to wake or "reverse" anesthesia if necessary]. Actually making the decisions and assessing. If there's a rough recovery, they put that on us and say like, "Okay, what are your thoughts?" . . . That's kind of nice. I feel like I get caught up in the hospital a lot where it's like I'm learning, but I'm also—I just feel like I'm not because I just kind of do what I have to do because I have to ask three, five, whatever how many people like, "What about this? Is this okay? What about this?"

For students in this liminal stage, having the decision-making ability and being referred to as "doctor" was a critical transitional moment in their self-perception and understanding.

Laura, remembering one of her early blocks in oncology, speaks directly to this transitional space,

I guess that's where I'm—because I keep going back to [talking about] oncology but seeing my first few patients that—I don't know. When an owner was crying, I could start crying right now. So I feel like I'm still kind of trying to figure out, I have to be the doctor and be strong for them, but then I still have an emotional component of it, which goes back to the compassion and empathy, like putting myself where they are and how I would handle things if that was my situation.

For Laura, being the "doctor" means sublimating her own emotions, a lesson that she has learned through her first three years at CMU. As the veterinary literature attests, this emotional detachment is still widely expected and modeled in the veterinary profession (Hulsbergen et al., 2019). Laura was conscious that part of what she needed to learn through her clinical rotations is how to first control and then eliminate her emotions, a particularly challenging task in the field of oncology.

For others, the first steps into becoming a doctor meant learning to use the impersonal, detached language that is modeled for them in the veterinary hospital. It was not unusual in these interviews for students—from all tracks and specialties—to refer to animals as "things" and "stuff," language that I had not heard in earlier interviews. Brandon, who uses more respectful terms (e.g., "anyone"), still employs detached language when I ask him about difficult situations he had faced in the past year,

I don't think anyone was euthanized. I mean, there are some, I think, that come through ECC [Emergency Critical Care] that end up getting euthanized because they just can't afford the surgeries through ortho. As far as any negative outcomes, I don't think anyone had any really bad. There's Coco. She was a chronic abuse case, this cocker spaniel. But they had put pins in the tibiotarsal joint, I think. And those had started to come out, so she had this big wound. And you could kind of see—you could see the pins when you looked in there. So that was less than ideal. But she felt fine, I think. So overall, nothing crazy.

Brandon's language suggested that this is all normal in veterinary medicine, from the chronic abuse to the situation with the pins being "less than ideal," to "nothing crazy." As he actively thought and talked to me, he also integrated these experiences into what is reasonable and to be expected in the veterinary profession, and thus not worthy of emotional investment. This use of a common language is an intrinsic component of communities of practice (Lave & Wenger, 1991). Individuals entering those communities learn to share knowledge and at a very basic level communicate with each other, as O'Brien and Bates (2015) investigated in their study of aviation students and Klass (1987/2010) reflected on in her memoir of medical school. However, as Lave and Wenger (1991) also explore, this language use is not innocent and value-free: instead, the language that is used also creates meaning. In Brandon's case, the language that he had absorbed in the teaching hospital defined and produced his idea of what is normal and to be expected as a veterinarian.

Learning to emotionally detach was also an important, if difficult lesson for Kiara, who describes in intense details her experience doing an internship at a USDA facility, where cats were intentionally bred for research that ends in pain and death.[3]

> At the research facility, just knowing that some of the animals weren't going to make it, I was especially mindful of becoming attached. Like some of the research they were doing, they weren't going to have the best outcome. If I got there and they were gone, I knew where they were going and I was kind of like, oh man, they told me not to get attached, but I got attached, that type of thing. That was just kind of hard to deal with. . . . I knew, with this research in particular they were going to be sick, and they were not going to feel well, and then eventually they were euthanized, if they didn't pass away on their own first. It was tough, but I know the reason behind it, and I know why they are doing it, and how it's beneficial. Unfortunately, that's the way that it has to be done, there's no other way to do it, as far as I know. It was kind of difficult seeing, yeah, you can get good results at the end, there's a benefit to animals in the future that are going through it, but just knowing that these animals in themselves are like bred for it, it was kind of sad.
>
> It's kind of tough, because when you see them, you don't think they are going to be used and euthanized, you just think of someone owning them and loving them, taking care of them. Not to say that that wasn't done in this situation, whenever we went there to let some of them out, we would pet them, and we would groom them and everything, they were taken care of amazingly, but still at the same time.

Kiara tells me that the veterinary technicians working with the cats warned her not to become emotionally involved with the animals, but that, in fact, they had already formed close bonds with the cats in the research study. She explains,

> It's hard not to get attached when they're like, oh, this is Molly, this is Daisy. It's hard to not become attached when you've already given them a name. So it's like, who are you to tell me not to get attached when you are. It's kind of a practice what you preach type of thing, but it's kind of inevitable. You're taking care of this thing that's cute and cuddly, and cares for you too, and purrs when you come up to it and pet it. So it's kind of difficult to just do your job and not care. At the end of the day you can't help but care.

For one student, the emotional detachment that was necessary to become a veterinarian involved rethinking an earlier decision she had made in her life to adopt a vegetarian diet. Shanice tells me that her previous decision was based largely on emotion, and as she had learned the facts and science through veterinary school, she had resumed eating meat,

Shanice: I'm not one that likes the whole, "I'm not going to eat meat because of this." Because, well I did that actually so I first-hand know my reasoning behind it. Because I had done it with cattle in undergrad. I cut off eating beef for, it was about four years.

Nadine: Why did you do that?

Shanice: Because it's really dumb now but, at the time I just learned that dairy cattle, after they finish their time as dairy cattle, then they go on to become ground beef. So I didn't like the mindset of pretty much we use an animal for milk and then once they're done, we're just like, "Oh, forget you," and then you're—because I didn't like that aspect of it. But then once I learned more about it, I was like, "Okay, it's not"—that's not the straight process that happens. I feel like once you understand the whole picture it isn't just that cut and dry as you think. And then basically when they either can't give any more calves and milk or their milk isn't as productive, then that's when they go on to the beef industry and stuff. But yeah, and so I think the big thing with that is it's kind of necessary too, to meet the needs of humans and their beef intake. So it's kind of like the circle of life a little, so it makes more sense.

While the facts themselves have not changed, Shanice had (re)situated the reality within the discourse of the "milk industry" and the "beef industry," which allowed her to feel that the animal is serving a human purpose, and thus it is no longer an emotional issue or concern for her.

Yet later in the interview, Shanice again begins to wrestle with the emotions that she felt at a livestock auction on an exceedingly hot summer day, where she observed that the animals were not provided with water,

> In the livestock auctions, the big thing I saw about that was kind of like the treatment of animals, I guess. Like, it would kind of depend on the person that was working, but some of the people, they were kind of like really sweet to the animals, and then a lot of the other people had the mindset, we have so many animals in a short time frame. So they were a little more harsher with the animals I guess and didn't take it as slow as they need to. I also didn't like, when, how, animals get dropped off in the morning and the auction isn't until evening, the animals would go without water the whole time. Because if it's only a few hours, there's a rule that's okay to be the case. So I didn't like that, because I'm a believer that an animal always has to have to water, you know, it's hot, it's the summer, that wasn't kind of like the thinking of that.

Shanice's mentor, a veterinarian, explained that she was also troubled by it but as veterinarians there was little they could do but accept it as a legal and common practice,

> So my mentor I was with at the time, she had to really explain that I don't like it either, but there's nothing we can do, they're following regulations. So it was kind of, it helped solidify some of what I think about welfare, but then it also made me realize that there are limitations. There is only so much that you can make people do, if they are within the rules and regulations, they'll just argue back, this is fine. So I think that's the big thing I took out of that.

Despite Shanice's mentor's attempt to absolve the veterinary profession for responsibility for animal welfare (Arluke & Hafferty, 1996), Shanice left that day with strong misgivings about the way that the cows were treated, circling back to the topic later in our conversation,

> That really bothered me. Because even after we finished and I would go home. I would always have water. Like me and the vet, we always had water with us. Like I understand that the animals are bigger, so they have more water, they have that reserve. At the same time, I don't see how to justify that either.

As students move through this liminal phase, they are beginning to understand that their veterinary education is not prepared to assist them negotiate the suffering and pain that is an everyday part of the profession. Rollin (2019) suggests that this has been a constant in veterinary medicine for decades, and that the process of being forced to watch and participate in animal abuse, neglect, and trauma through the course of a veterinary education profoundly scars and shapes these beginning doctors.

STORIES OF CONNECTION: ANIMALS

As students started their clinical rotations, they began a process of relearning their connections to animals. For many students, these are the connections that featured prominently in the stories they told me as they entered veterinary school that are discussed in Chapter 3. Because there is limited (or no!) time for their emotions and limited space for investigation of ethical issues in the formal curriculum, students rely on their personal emotions and conversations with friends and colleagues to make sense of the wide range of animal encounters they experience. The intensity of these feelings is particularly strong during the early months of their clinical year, as students treat their first patients as "junior doctors." These are the patients and the experiences who will be formative of their professional identities. One of the students told me about how she left the hospital late at night, walked to her car, and sat in the car crying for an hour just to release the emotions that had built up before she could manage to drive home.

Many of the strongest emotions for animals during these interviews came from students who were doing their rotations in the large animal hospital, predominantly with animals destined for slaughter. Michelle recalls a particularly traumatizing situation with a calf,

> This calf that came in with an open tibial fracture, so bones sticking out, and it had happened two weeks ago. And so we knew that when it came in, it was probably not going to be fixable without surgery. And they're probably not going to want to do surgery because it's probably a feed lot calf, and it's just destined for market. So they got here and took radiographs, and it was definitely broken. The wound was this big with the bone sticking out, and it was all necrotic and disgusting. And the calf wasn't depressed. It was still bright. But the bone had healed so much already in the wrong way that there was no way we were going to be able to fix it without surgery.

So the clinician asked the people what his fate was. And they said, "Feed lot." And so he said that the bare minimum thing that we can do is cut off the exposed bone and just bandage him up and send him home with antibiotics. And then they can just send him to the feed lot and hope that he—and I asked him, and this was away from the clients, I was like, "Do you really think that animal is going to be able to be over 1,200 pounds and still be able to one, bear weight on that leg and two, not be in pain every single day and actually want to eat to put on that weight that they wanted to put on." And he's like, "Yeah, I think so." I didn't think that that—I didn't think that calf was going to make it to the feedlot. I really didn't think it was a good idea to not even offer euthanasia as an option. Offer what he said but also tell them that there's really not a good chance of that thing having a good quality of life until it goes to slaughter.

And so, then I talked to the resident later and asked for her opinion. And she's like, "Yeah, I really thought that calf should've been euthanized as well." So that was kind of hard, just seeing him doctor that calf up and send it home knowing that it's either going to die or it's going to be in pain its whole life.

As the calf leaves with his/her owner, Michelle is haunted by the reality of a life lived in pain on a feedlot, where the calf will eventually be slaughtered. Michelle does not discuss a particularly strong bond with the calf, and in fact, refers to the calf at points as "it" and "that animal." Despite that, she (and clearly in this case, the senior clinician) have strong concerns from the perspective of animal welfare about the quality of life of the calf. Yet, the calf, like most animals whom a veterinarian will encounter (with the exception of wildlife), has an owner. Animals are property, and while this social and legal concept is never fully discussed with students, it is always present. A persistent set of beliefs (or folklore) in veterinary medicine suggests that veterinarians function as either pediatricians or mechanics (Gage & Gage, 1993; Rollin, 2002; Ware, 2018). In the model that positions veterinarians as pediatricians—often in small or companion medicine—they are continually negotiating between the patient (animal) and the owner (human). Conversely, veterinarians are also compared to mechanics—usually in large or "food" animal medicine—because the philosophy and training often functions as if they were treating inanimate objects.

Yet there are important differences between human and animal medicine. Pediatricians treat humans, who do not have owners, and thus medical doctors can intervene if they feel that the welfare of a child is involved. While animal welfare laws in most states would allow a veterinarian to take action if a companion animal came into a veterinary hospital with bones sticking out that appeared to be the result of animal abuse, such laws do not extend to animals destined to food. Michelle learned that her emotional connection to the calf did not, and could not, change the outcome. Instead, in the large or "food" animal context, she is confronting a profession that largely sees itself within the mechanic analogy, even though it is scientifically inaccurate to believe that animals do not feel pain (Rollin, 2019).

In the large animal hospital, students have more limited contact with clients than is typical in the small hospital. That is one of the reasons that Michelle was able to clearly see and feel the calf's perspective: she had no direct contact with the owner as the senior clinician was responsible for that minimal contact. Thus, these experiences with sick, injured, and dying animals, whose only value to humans is economic, are profoundly challenging for students.

In other instances in the large animal hospital, animals are companions, and they have owners who value them emotionally. Yet, even in these cases, large animal hospitals are not designed for human visitors.[4] Given the reality that there are few other humans present, students have enhanced opportunities to get to know and interact with animals. Stephanie relates an experience with a sheep, Duncan, and her strong feelings that Duncan was suffering,

> So there was a sheep that came in. His name was Duncan. He was blind. He was having seizures. It was a bad situation. They'd noticed it on a Saturday. He didn't come in until Tuesday because they didn't have a way to bring him into the hospital. He had very little brain function left. He really wasn't surviving, but it was the stepdad's pet sheep which, I mean, he was 250 pounds so it's not like he was little. And he [the stepdad] had since passed away, so the family was having a really hard time letting him go. And I had a very, very hard time with it. Because he couldn't see, he was seizing every 30 minutes to hour, he wasn't recovering with anything we were giving him, there was no progress.
>
> And I actually went up to Dr. Smythe and I was like, "I'm having a really hard time with this." I said, "This is very inhumane to me and I don't think this should be happening and I'm not going to be able to be on this case very much longer if we continue just to put fluids and keep the sheep alive for no reason." And he told me, he goes, we're giving it 24 hours, that's what we told her [the client]. And then the decision will be made to euthanize. And I mean, and then we euthanized him. And I mean it was awesome because it's, they just go. They just go, and they're at peace, they're not seizing. It just, it was very, very difficult for me because it was hard—I felt like I could empathize with the client. But at the same time my place was with that sheep, and it's like, he's not living. He's not living, he can't function, he's seizing. He's not responding to anything. How in the world can you keep this thing alive? I thought it was very, very not appropriate. So I just dealt with it. And luckily it was kind of a 48-hour thing. So I didn't have to deal with it as long.
>
> I never thought I would but with Duncan, I never thought I would say this but it went through my mind to euthanize him because he was in so much pain. I know I could have never done that but for me to actually have that thought, I was so upset because it's like, I shouldn't have to be thinking about a way to safely and effectively euthanize this animal because of how much pain it's in because its owners will not put it down. And I understand that's not my decision but at the same time, it's your [my] case. I can't take myself off of that because I want nothing to do with it.

Despite Stephanie's earlier critiques (discussed in Chapter 4) of the "small animal mentality," and the fact that she refers to Duncan as a "thing" in some of the aforementioned narratives, she also clearly says that "my place was with that sheep." While she knows that legally she cannot euthanize Duncan, like Michelle, she is in the process of learning about her connections to animals and the difficult situations that she is being exposed to through her veterinary education.

Because euthanasia is a viable and legal option in veterinary medicine, as opposed to human medicine, it becomes the inflection point for students' emotions (Morris, 2012). In Michelle and Stephanie's stories, they both identify with an animal whose pain they feel intensely. Nicole tells a similar story about Misty, a horse who was her patient in the large animal hospital. Misty was a companion animal who had been in and out of the large animal hospital through the extended period that I conducted my interviews. I had heard her story from several students. Nicole was on the rotation when Misty was finally euthanized,

> She was lame. So first, she originally came in with a foot abscess or something. And then she chronically had foot abscesses. And then the last time she came in, one of her joints became septic, so they were trying to manage that. And they kept getting more and more aggressive with the treatment. When I took over for—she was in a cast. Her foot was so septic and so diseased that they'd cut a hole in the side of the hoof. And they had put a catheter into the joint, and they were trying to treat with antibiotics.
>
> I only had her for four days before we euthanized her. And they were due to change the cast on Friday, and the clinician says, "Oh, well, we have time," and this was on Thursday, "We have time. Let's just go ahead and change the cast now." When we took it off, her foot had almost completely sloughed off. And he was like, "This lady had spent—ah, she's probably spent over hundreds of thousands of dollars on this horse". She also had another horse that had seven colic surgeries here that also lived in the hospital for six months at a time who she euthanized a couple of months ago.
>
> The clinician that was on this case, Dr. Hendricks, is way more willing than the other clinicians. He'll take on cases that everyone else is like, "No, that's hopeless. There's nothing we can do for that." He's willing to try just about anything. And if they're willing to pay for it—they're willing to go the distance, he's willing to try for them. And we took that cast off, and he goes, "I've got to call her right now." He's like, "This is the end of the line." And he's—"All right. There's nothing else I can do for her." And so we had a long conversation on the phone with her. She was naturally very upset. He came back, and he said, "Okay, she's coming in an hour." And he goes, "We're going to inject some dye into a vein to see if there's any blood flow left of the foot." When she came in, that's what they'd decided. He goes, "Okay, we really need to euthanize. There's nothing else we can do for her."
>
> She was in horrible pain for months. I felt so incredibly bad for this horse. She could barely walk.

Like Stephanie, Nicole had serious concerns about how horses under her care were suffering, and eventually took those concerns to the clinician,

> So I feel like I'm trying to see it through the animal's eyes. I did have a clinician on this block tell me that—so I wanted to give pain medication for something, and he said, "No, they don't need it." He goes, "Horses don't feel pain like we do. They have a higher tolerance," and I'm like, "Do they really? Do you actually know that"? And he let me give her the medication. He's like, "If it will make you feel better." I was like, "It will make me feel better, and I'm sure it'll make him feel better, too." So there are some clinicians that don't—they're very light on the pain medication they give, and he has been throughout the whole block. He doesn't necessarily think they need as much pain medication as other clinicians do, and I just feel like the procedures that we perform on them, I imagine them being performed on me, and I'm like, "This has to be awfully painful." Even if you're hiding your pain better, I really find it hard to believe that they're not feeling it to as great of an extent. Even if they're not showing it, it doesn't mean they're not feeling it. Some people, just like some animals, are a little more stoic than others, but it doesn't mean that they don't deserve a little bit of drugs to help them feel better.

As Nicole tells it, the clinician allowed her to administer additional pain medication to the horse, but in a way that dismissed and minimized Nicole's concerns for the horse's welfare and her attempt to understand the animal's perspective. Nicole is struck by what she perceives as the callousness of the clinician and the clinician's lack of interest, which seems to be at odds with what she understands as the core of the veterinary profession, animal health, and welfare. Yet, as a student, she can do little.

While the logistics of a large animal hospital create a focus on the animal with the owner or client a constant but largely distant presence, the reality is quite different in the small animal hospital. While the small animal hospital does treat some animals from shelters and rescues in the area, most of the animals (predominantly dogs and cats) who are patients there have owners who are intimately involved in the treatment plans and decision making for their companions and are also regular visitors to the hospital. At the small animal hospital, students are also assigned (in most cases) as the primary contact with clients and are required to update them daily while the animal is hospitalized. As a result, most of the stories that students tell about their relationships with small animals are filtered through their interactions with human clients. There were a few exceptions, however, where students stepped back from their immersion in the human world and took the perspective of the animal.

Christina talks about her experience caring for a rambunctious puppy who other technicians, students, and clinicians were wary of,

> There were a lot of struggles with him. Mainly, there's some people who just hated him because there's a "will bite" sign on his cage, even though with me, he was really nice.
>
> And so he just had a really bad reputation with people, and then once you start off that way—. . . people were like, "Oh, he's going to bite," so they think they have to go in and manhandle him. But I'm like, "I've been working with him for a week." So it was kind of frustrating for me because a lot of people were really negative towards him, but he was a really good dog. Like when you walked him and stuff, he wasn't aggressive at all, and it was guessing he was getting annoyed but I'm like, "He's a five-month-old puppy that's been stuck in this little cage for a week now. He gets walked a few times a day. He doesn't get to run around and play. He has this big cone on his head. He just wants to be a puppy."

Finally, Heather tells me a story about a cat, Gracie, who came to the small animal hospital with end stage kidney disease,

> I really liked Gracie. Gracie was a very thin, frail, little sweet thing that I spend a lot of time with her trying to help her become comfortable. I made a cat bed out of towels and just a lot of time trying to be gentle and everything, and it was really nice to see as she started to feel better she acted more cat-like and would start to make a fuss when we'd draw blood and that was just really nice seeing her almost come back to life. We talked a lot with mom about quality-of-life stuff at home because we knew we weren't going to be able to fix her, you can't fix kidney disease.
>
> I'm interested in the euthanasia aspect, so it was really enjoyable for me to talk with her about when you get home really monitor to make sure Gracie doesn't start suffering. But what was really sad was I thought that we bought her maybe a month [through

treatment at the hospital] and then I woke up to a text today and had seen that Gracie had been brought back to the ER this morning, so she'd only gone back for a week and then they brought her back in to euthanize this morning.

And honestly, I feel like—well, definitely the intern I was working with wanted to find a reason, almost, to euthanize the cat because she perceived that the cat was really suffering.

Heather's connection to Gracie grows through her daily routine of taking care of her in the intensive care unit at the hospital, and as Heather explains, both Heather and the intern on the case struggle with releasing Gracie back to her family. They feel that they can take better care of and prevent Gracie's suffering at the hospital, and perhaps find a medical reason to euthanize her sooner.

Students' final year of their veterinary education is relentless. There is little to no time to reflect, to think, and to feel. Yet, strong emotions for and with their animal patients dominate the beginning of this liminal period for students. For most students, they want to see the world through the eyes of their animal patients and are confronted by a structure that often prohibits or restricts that perspective. Certainly, at this point in their veterinary education, students' medical judgement may be limited: it is entirely possible that students tended to think euthanasia was required when decades of clinical practice might suggest otherwise. At the beginning of this clinical year, students' hearts are open to animals. But animals remain property in the human world, and thus while humans are sometimes not physically present with the animals, their needs, desires, and priorities are always first. In the following section, I turn to explore students' early lessons about working with humans in veterinary medicine.

LEARNING HUMANS

In the world of veterinary practice, most veterinarians spend their days balancing between their animal patients and their human clients, who ultimately dictate what happens to their patients. There are of course, some exceptions: veterinarians who treat wildlife at rescue centers and those who work with companion animal shelters have less interactions with humans, and do not have consider a human's desires and directives when treating patients. But for most students in my study, their career path will take them into regular, frequent contact with humans who place varying degrees and kinds of value on the animals they own. For veterinarians following the small animal and companion tracks, they will regularly work with humans who have emotional connections to their animal patients. For those on the large animal tracks, the value of the animal patients is, with some limited exceptions, solely economic.

For students doing clinical rotations in the small animal hospital, interactions with human owners are a constant part of their responsibility. In most cases, fourth-year students are the primary contact point between the owner and the hospital and are required to contact the owners regularly with updates on the animals. There is, of course, substantial variability in these interactions, both from the perspective of the students and the owners. Some owners refuse to talk to the students, demanding to speak with a clinician. In other cases, owners welcome the opportunity to talk, at length, about their animal, and can consume hours of a student's day on the phone. For students, they are acutely aware that they cannot leave the hospital at the end of the day until they have updated each client and completed all necessary paperwork. A client who talks for an hour can be a major source of frustration, as the student watches the clock, knowing that with each passing minute there will be less sleep that night before the early morning return to the hospital.

Yet, students do feel a personal connection to some clients. Heather explains to me that students are the ones who take the responsibility for sympathy cards when a patient dies,

> There are cards that the hospital provides that we should make when an animal passes away and they said some students decide to get their own cards that are nicer, and I really had a good time taking care of Gracie. Gracie was a sweet cat and I feel so badly for her mom that I just really wanted to do this.

Heather then pulls the card out to show to me,

> So yeah, I got this really cute card for her and I'm going to bring it in for the ECC [Emergency Critical Care] folks. I just want you to see how cute it is [laughter]—bring it back for the ECC folks to sign.

Positive feedback from human clients can also help support students and allow them an emotional release and connection to their work that is impossible with their supervisors. Anna talked about her interactions with a client whose dog had been a patient of hers before dying shortly thereafter,

> I've had owners that were going through difficult times with their dogs. And I would talk to them on the phone about it. And then we sent one of our patients home that had a surgery where we weren't sure if they were going to make it or not because it was a big surgery. But he was doing really well when he left the hospital. And I was talking with the owners, and she was so happy with how things were going at home. And then all of the sudden, the next week she called and said he wasn't doing well. And since this owner lived two hours away, we suggested that she go to her local vet and have some bloodwork done to see how he was doing. And before she could make it to the vet he just died at home. And that was hard. And I talked with the owner afterwards, and we kind of talked about everything that happened. And she was still very appreciative of me and the clinician putting so much work into the dog. And she mentioned after everything that she really appreciated that I seemed to take interest in her dog and that I actually cared and spent time with him while he was here. So that was touching as well.

Students were not only emotionally affected by their own relationships with animals, but by the connections that they witnessed between the clients and their animals. Alison told me a story about an owner who brought his bird into the hospital as an emergency. Because CMU does not have an avian specialty service and the cockatoo was in distress, the bird was diverted to a general, community-oriented service in the hospital. The cockatoo came in with a prolapsed cloaca (vent), was in shock, and not breathing. Alison, the student who talked with the client, tells me that she was deeply affected by the story of the 20-year relationship between the bird and the human owner,

> He was telling me the story about how—so this bird has kind of been with him throughout a lot of his life and a lot of his ups and downs and all that. So originally he had this bird with a previous girlfriend and then they split up and the girl took the bird. And then, eventually, he got it back. And there's all this other—a lot of back-and-forth. But the one thing that's kind of been consistent in his life is he's always had a really strong attachment to this bird. And so even when something—maybe things don't go well at work or he loses his job or something, he has to switch careers—things of that sort where this bird has kind of been, always, the center of all that is good in his life, in a way.
>
> But that made it all that much harder to see when this bird was dying how hard that was hitting him. And kind of listening to all those stories he has and how much he clearly loves this pet of his. And he had a really hard time, at least initially kind of processing what was happening. Because he kept asking, "Is there any chance that she could be alive? Can we try the shock thing? What's that shock thing that they do on TV; can you do that?" And we were trying to explain to him, well, this isn't the case that that would even work, even if—that's a totally separate situation that you would use that in. And he was asking us to try anything and all that. And then afterwards, once we determined that the bird—there was no getting it back, and he finally kind of came to terms with it, he kind of went through this other—a little bit where he was trying to blame himself. He was like, "If I had gotten earlier—if I had seen it earlier—" because it took him a little while to actually notice the problem. And a lot of kind of self-blame, and we're trying to—because, at this point, I was using the room. I was doing my paperwork for the case and Dr. Morris was still with him. And so he was saying how—he was trying to console him, "You know, this percentage of birds that come in with this don't survive and that really is a hard thing to catch, and it really is a hard thing to treat for and you did what you could," and kind of try and console a little bit and say it's not his fault; it happens. So it was kind of interesting seeing him go through these different phases of—I guess it was kind of like phases of grief.

OPENINGS: SEEING THE PATH FORWARD

As the students in my study finish their third year and begin their final clinical rotations, they enter a period of transitional liminality in their lives. At this moment students are freed from the constraints of the day-to-day drudgery of lectures, studying, memorizing, and exams. They feel that they are finally on their path to becoming: becoming veterinarians, becoming doctors, and leaving their student identities behind as they enter the wilds. At this critical juncture, the students are particularly open to learning about the veterinary profession, about themselves, about their relationships to animals, and to other humans. What is remarkable about this moment—particularly in comparison to multiple other points in this study—is how they are actively thinking about and seeking opportunities to learn. They are eager, excited, and ready. Alison's excitement at learning how to intubate a possum, in a conversation filled with laughter, is one example. There is joy for many students at finally being able to apply what they had learned over the past two years: that there actually is an end to all that tedium, and that perhaps it had a purpose.

There are many "firsts," as is to be expected. Perhaps the situations in which students find themselves are not totally new: cumulatively the students in my study had tens of thousands of hours of experience with animals in multiple veterinary, research, farm, and other contexts even before starting veterinary school. What (or perhaps more accurately, who) is different was themselves. This is the first time they are doing, seeing, smelling, feeling, and experiencing as the veterinarian they are becoming (Ware, 2018). They begin to step outside of a lay perspective and to move into what they have been taught and perceived to be the role of the veterinarian. This movement is expressed by students such as Christina, who is so proud and happy in moments "in the wild" when she is called "doctor" and could make decisions, and equally miserable when she is stuck in the hierarchies of the teaching hospital where she is a mere student.

Suddenly, the students are seeing the world from a fresh perspective, they are at a yet another beginning, one that is very different from when they entered vet-erinary school two and a half years earlier. At that point, they knew they were still students and what lay ahead was two plus years of stasis, not change. Now, as the students start their clinical year, they are thrust into contexts that are *both* familiar and strange, because they see and position themselves differently. This period of transitional liminality made them particularly open to learning. Much of what the students experience and learn, however, is emotionally painful and difficult. In their role as junior doctors, they cannot not step away: they are required to confront their feelings and begin to internalize the responsibility that they have to their animal patients. Stephanie's earlier quote encapsulates this new reality, "And I understand that's not my decision but at the same time, it's your [my] case. I can't take myself off of that because I want nothing to do with it." With no real authority and no medical license, they can do little for the animals in their care except comfort them and con-nect with them, in whatever way they could, and thus that is what they do. Because of this structural reality, this is a period of intense emotion and openness to animals and their experiences. Ware (2018) reflects on how veterinary professionals in her research discuss their connections with the "spirit" of animal,

> For many veterinary professionals, physical and sensory (including touch, texture, smell, and sounds) interactions with animal bodies play a major role in recognizing nonhuman animals as individuals and sentient beings. Sometimes they refer to the essence of an animal as its spirit.

(p. 21)

Students feel these connections the strongest because they are the ones who are often responsible for the nursing care. Ware (2018) tells a story from her fieldwork of a fourth-year veterinary student who had developed a strong bond with a turtle in her care,

> Among my most poignant fieldwork memories is seeing a fourth-year vet student weep over the death of a sick turtle she had been nursing for several days. This anonymous

turtle was one of many hundreds hatched at a commercial turtle breeding operation where a mysterious pathogen was killing turtles. It, along with several other turtles, was delivered to the vet school not for treatment, but to try to identify the disease. The vet student responsible for its care, however, had grown fond of her patient, tried to heal it, and grieved when it died.

(p. 22)

Andrew tells me a related story about being responsible for the care for Charlie, a dog who was in the small animal hospital,

> So I think one of the things I learned about working with animals as far as patient care and nursing care in general is it was really frustrating but also really rewarding. A lot of my day was just spent trying to keep Charlie clean, dry, and comfortable for periods of time. That was just a lot of getting slings on him to walk him out, cleaning him up when he got urine or poop on himself, and keeping his kennel clean, and icing his incision and then heating his incision, and doing PT. It's a lot of time-consuming stuff that, at times, was really frustrating but then also it was really rewarding as I saw him get better and also as I could, talking to his family, know that I'd been doing everything I could to get him on track to do well and that I was taking good care of him.

Yet, as Andrew and I conclude this part of the conversation, he observes that nursing care will not be a regular part of his job as a veterinarian: the personal, emotional work of the profession is done by the nurses/technicians.[5] As a veterinarian, he will need to learn to prioritize scientific ways of knowing and to forget those moments in which he loves animals.

In the next chapter, I return to the students and their stories as they near the end of their veterinary education. By this time, students have completed almost all their required clinical rotations and have most have passed their veterinary licensing exam. Like Andrew, the students have now learned that their love of animals is largely irrelevant to their daily world. Consumed by their own intense, difficult, and exhausting schedule, their struggles with other people, and their need to negotiate their place in a veterinary profession they still do not fully understand, animals are largely forgotten.

NOTES

1 The exception to this is students who are participating in any international externships or off-campus blocks. The veterinary college at CMU requires a quarantine period after returning from veterinary or other animal facilities outside of the United States, as a biohazard precaution. Thus, students who complete an international block that ends, for example, on a Saturday, cannot fly home on Sunday and begin a new block at the CMU veterinary hospital on Monday. Given this requirement, students who completed any international blocks were required to take the following block as vacation, which many students used for travel.

2 Comparatively, it is remarkable how different the interview scheduling process was when I contacted students to arrange their final interviews. At that point, they had completed 17 or 18 of the required 19 rotations. They felt free to come and go from their responsibilities,

many confided in me that they no longer read their end-of-rotation evaluations, and most had little concern for what their supervisors thought of them. Many stayed and talked to me for almost 2 hours.

3 Shortly after my interview with Kiara, the cat research that she describes from her experience the previous year was exposed by the White Coat Waste Project and labeled the "kitten cannibalism" project. After a public outcry, extensive media coverage and the involvement of many members of Congress, the USDA shutdown the research. For details about the research and the circumstances that led to its exposure and closure, see Goodman (2018) and Romo (2019). For reaction from the scientific community, see Wadman (2019). I discuss my own experiences of my struggles with the content of many interviews, including this one, in Chapter 9.

4 "Esther the Wonder Pig" provides a real-life example of the challenges faced by large animal owners in trying to spend time with an animal who is hospitalized in a large animal veterinary hospital. Esther, a 500–600-pound pig, is a companion animal, and a media and social media star (see Jenkins & Walter, 2016). Esther also a webpage (www.estherthe wonderpig.com/), and accounts on Facebook, Instagram, and Twitter). Esther faced month-long stays at the Ontario Veterinary Hospital when she was treated for breast cancer and foot problems that required multiple surgeries. Through their social media accounts, Esther's fathers (Steve and Derek) documented their struggle to sleep with her in her stall, even moving in living room furniture so that she would feel more at home. While this situation is extraordinary, it demonstrates the challenges of supporting human–animal connections in large animal hospital environments.

5 The older language is "veterinary technician." Recently, there has been a shift in the profession to "veterinary nurse."

6 Endings
There Are No Animals Here

In the spring of 2019, the students in my study were rapidly approaching graduation. Most (not all) had passed the national veterinary boards (North American Veterinary Licensing Exam, or NAVLE) the previous fall. Except for the students who were awaiting placement from the United States Department of Agriculture, all had firm plans for employment after graduation. One by one, spread over the last month of their veterinary education, they joined me one final time in a conference room at the veterinary college. By this point, the students were in their 16th or 17th clinical rotation: they were no longer beginners. There were a few exceptions: one student told me she had had a serious medical problem and had to take medical leave for several months. Others were slightly behind because they had failed a class (or an early clinical rotation). To graduate, students had to complete all clinical rotations, which meant that a few students would not be able to finish and leave until later in the summer.

These final interviews were the longest of the entire study, many lasting for almost two hours. Many of these conversations were intensely emotional, and I believe cathartic for some of my participants. Students were mentally exhausted, and the experiences, feelings, and unspoken words of the last year poured out in unfiltered streams.

The title of this book is *Learning Animals*. Throughout the book, I focus on what my participants learn about their relationships with animals through their veterinary education, and how the structural realities of veterinary education shape that experience, producing a particular curriculum and a specific pedagogical experience. And while animals are still the reason for this book, they play only a peripheral role in this chapter, as the supporting cast for the main story of human relationships, hierarchies, emotion, and often pain that dominates the students' final year. The participants in my study never fully expected this reality and were largely unprepared for it. Throughout the year and my final interviews, they continually try to reach back and reconnect with animals and their original purpose in becoming a veterinarian. Some are successful, for fleeting moments in time. Yet, overall, the curriculum and pedagogy of their final year of veterinary education pushes them away from animals. Instead of the psychological paradigms that dominate the analysis of the veterinary student experience (Holden, 2020; Karaffa & Hancock, 2019, 2019a; Liu & van Gelderen, 2020) in this chapter, I stress the structural and pedagogical nature of these experiences. Through these intense clinical rotations in the fourth year, students are moving through a state of transitional liminality, and in these moments are learning about what it means to be a veterinarian, and the multiple connections and disconnections—some hidden, some visible—that are a part of the veterinary profession.

DOI: 10.1201/9781003269984-6

In Chapter 5, students such as Christina talk proudly about the fleeting moments during which they are referred to as a doctor. In this earlier, transitional space, they are aware that they are still students and that the times that they are allowed to "be the doctor" are ones to be savored and remembered. By the time I meet with them almost a year later, students talk boldly and firmly about "my profession"—they identify with the veterinary profession. For example, Jennifer tells me about the struggles she felt during her Emergency Critical Care rotation, when faced with an animal she perceived was suffering, and a client who did not feel ready to euthanize,

> People who, especially, don't have money or don't have ways to manage things that—or like some of the sick animals that really, really need help, but the owner for one reason or another, money, whatever other reason, doesn't want to let us help and wants to take it home. And it's really hard to accept that sometimes. Because you just want to help them, and the animal is suffering. But you can't do anything about that. That's difficult for me. I'm sure most people feel the same in *my* profession.

(my emphasis)

Note that Jennifer clearly claims her membership in the veterinary profession, using the possessive "my." As she does this, she moves herself further from the student role (which she still, technically, inhabits) through a transitional space in which she might have tentatively claimed the title of "veterinarian" to a full embracing of the profession and her position in it.

Indeed, as most of the students have passed the veterinary board exams by the time of our meeting, they are within weeks of becoming licensed veterinarians. Because they now identify as veterinarians, my participants have fully rejected the positionality of "student" and constantly resist that self-categorization. The students' imaginings of their relationships with animals are always filtered through this new lens of "being a veterinarian."

As I discussed in Chapter 2, in the context of medical education, Goldberg (2008) explores the conflict between what he terms "humanism" and "professionalism" in medical education, and the way that the medical curriculum shapes students' identity as they move through the process of becoming doctors. Goldberg argues that as students transition during their medical education, they begin to prioritize their duty to their profession over their lay or humanist values. All decisions, ethical and moral judgements, and ways of being are filtered through their emergent professional identity, as humanistic ways of being and thinking fade.

This pattern of movement is evident in the students who participate in my study. They learn and largely accept that there are ways of being a veterinarian, certain approaches to problems, and allowable ways to relate to both humans and animals. At this point, the students realize that their veterinary education was not fully defined by the basic science classes that they slogged through during their first two years, but in the mores and ways of being that they observe and absorb in the veterinary teaching hospital and in their externships and off-campus experiences throughout the world. However, as I suggested in Chapter 4, the groundwork for this acceptance is set during those early years, as students are required to experience animals in ways that they have not previously, for example, through the requirement to snare a pig and kill a chicken. Those experiences produce a collective veterinary identity, one which accepts that the profession is segmented (Vermilya, 2015). Even though a small animal track student may feel discomfort with some of these procedures, they come to accept and trust the decision making of their colleagues, who in many cases are their friends, roommates, and sometimes romantic partners. This is where and how "professionalism" is developed, allowing for a learned acquiescence that then (in theory, at least) carries them through to graduation. Despite their overall acceptance of professionalism as the dominant paradigm for their thinking, there are moments of critique and resistance, where they assert their humanism and use a different lens for understanding and connecting with the humans and animals who populate their daily lives.

In this chapter, I explore students' experiences during their final year of veterinary education. I first discuss the students themselves and what they experience, putting their voices and perspectives at the center. I then examine how they shape and understand their connections and disconnections with humans, as they begin to understand that human emotions, desires, feelings, and decisions are at the core of the lived, day-to-day rhythm of the veterinary profession. I move into a conversation about how students react to this intense, emotional year through adjustment to the realities of the profession and the twin dynamic of sporadic resistance combined with the actuality and/or hope of renewal. Finally, I explore the meaning that students make of the veterinary oath. These words symbolize their shift from a lay into a professional role. Yet, as I discuss, few students have had the will, opportunity, or requirement to think about what these words mean and how they may shape their possible veterinary futures.

HOW THE JOURNEY ENDS: ANXIETY, STRESS, AND EXHAUSTION

As I discussed in Chapter 5, when I met with the students as they began their clinical rotations, they are excited and hopeful. Each of them has carefully planned this final, fourth year, one that they have anticipated eagerly since starting veterinary school. Yet, as I meet students for our final interviews, they are anxious, stressed, and exhausted. Many are unhappy—some deeply bitter—about their experiences during their clinical year. For example, Heather is very blunt when I asked her to give me an overview of the past year,

> I don't feel like a student. I feel like an indentured slave. It's so frustrating. There's just a lot of things that we do that they say is for us becoming a doctor, but it feels more like we are free labor for the school. Like doing things like ICU duty and around call shifts and everything is just really unfortunate because I feel like it impairs our learning because when I'm here until 2:00 in the morning until 6:00 the next day that impairs my learning when I can't sleep.

Similarly, Anna was extremely emotional when we met, as she lets her feelings about the past year come out after many months of simply pushing to be able to finish veterinary school,

Yeah. I just haven't really talked about a lot of the stuff. I just keep shoving it down, just to get through it. Now that it's over, I haven't actually let it out, yet. So I'm sorry it had to be here . . . and I've been hearing about it, with all of these end-of-the-year curriculum reviews, where people are just being mistreated by people in the hospital because of stress. And everybody's understaffed—we're completely understaffed in the hospital and all the technicians are angry from it, and they're taking it out on us. And we don't feel like we're being given the attention, in terms of education, as we need to. We just feel like we're being taken advantage of, and it hurts to hear that some people, where they've lost important people in their life and they just want to take time off to deal with their emotions and life, and they're being denied it because we're so busy that they can't let any of us take personal time. I've just been listening to all these stories, and I consider myself a very empathetic person, and it just really hurts.

And I've felt frustrated, in general, just about the amount I feel like we're over-worked, and I get frustrated because nobody wants to talk to me about my case. They're just bossing me around to go do stuff. . . . I've had days where I just get really, really angry because I feel like the only time I've been involved with my patient is when I've been told to do paperwork on them. I'm not being included on things with the case and then I start to get frustrated because it's like, "Why am I here? I'm just here to write the paperwork and physically push the medications and feed the animal and walk it." It's just I'm not here to do that. But I don't mind doing that stuff but if I'm so busy doing that to where I can't be included in the doctor conversations, that's when I start to have a problem with it.

Heather and Anna's emotions were exceptionally intense through our conversations, though the feelings of being used and exploited as free labor for the veterinary hospital during their fourth year were a constant theme throughout most of the interviews. Like a human teaching hospital, the CMU veterinary teaching hospital follows a highly structured and hierarchical system, consisting of fourth-year students at the bottom, followed by interns, residents, and attendings. Thus, for students to actually do anything remotely resembling what a doctor might do, they had to consult multiple layers of people above them and wait for answers. Alex explains what he feels like when he is trying to help a patient and a client, yet is powerless within this system,

Yeah, and then also—and also you're stuck with having to wait for the people above you to make the decision, so you're just antsy and you're like, "Oh my God. I'm here." And I'm like, "This guy's yelling at me when things going to get done?" And I'm just like, "I don't know. I'm trying to find another guy to help get things moving along." I think that's the anxiety and discomfort with that.

While Heather and Anna were focused on small animal medicine, and spent most of their campus-based rotations in the small animal hospital, Christina relates a similar experience in her rotations in the large animal hospital,

What I learned about vet school. It's rough. It's really hard, and a lot of times I feel like it could be better because I feel like the hospital's understaffed as far as doctors go, as far as technicians go, which I think is a bigger deal. A lot of times I feel like I'm just doing tech work and paperwork, and I'm not doing things that I'll be doing as a doctor, as expected of me in my job. So I had a lot of frustrations with just being free labor for this hospital. . . . You just can't help but build up these negative emotions, which I don't really like to have.

Students following a mixed track were generally required to do several large animal focused rotations, and they were particularly upset about their time spent in the large animal hospital. For example, Brianna tells me,

I'm telling you this year—I feel like this school has aged me 23 years in this four-year period. . . . So the large animal hospital has issues. It's very understaffed so people are very stressed out. I think there is still a component of just general personality and how people are but I think that some intricacies of personalities are further highlighted when people are stressed out so there was a lot of yelling, and I don't do well with that. I can take feedback and help but not in the form of yelling. So that was really hard for me of just the way that we were treated and just kind of expected to do a lot and give up a lot of our time but being treated like we weren't worth anything.

Much of the students' time in the hospital was spent under the supervision of experienced veterinary nurses (technicians), who had some authority over the students. Not surprisingly, the students began to resent the nurses' authority, as they were on the path to becoming doctors while the nurses would remain as nurses. Student complaints about the nurses (technicians) were frequent, including that they were often lazy, arrogant, disrespectful of the veterinary students, and favored the veterinary nursing students. Erin's story was typical. As she relates in the following, she was trying to listen to the doctors' conversations about a patient, when the nurse pulled her away for what she considered a menial task,

There was a time when I was trying to look at radiographs of my dog and I was trying to listen to what the doctors were saying and kind of learn what was going on with him but then I got called away by a technician to make a clay paw.[1] And I was just like, "I really want to listen into the discussion about the patient because it's my patient and I want to be involved."

Michelle tells me how she coped with the realities of the teaching hospital and her disappointment in her experiences there during her clinical year,

I like to think of myself as pretty tough, so it doesn't affect me as much as it affects other people. You just kind of learn to brush off everything. And I do feel bad for the people because one of the residents can be extremely harsh, and she uses words that are not appropriate and just talks really awful to people. And not everyone can just brush it off, and so I do feel bad for the people that can't because it really affects how you perform. And then combine that with sleep deprivation during those blocks, it's just a double whammy. I mean, everyone knows that there's flaws in the system, but no one really does anything to fix it. And I think that's more frustrating than not having the experience that I really imagined, I guess.

Michelle, like most students in this study, enjoyed her rotations off campus, as she felt there was treated with respect. Students were almost unanimously enthusiastic about their off-campus experiences, explaining how they were able to be a doctor and make decisions in those contexts. In the wild of the real world, they were freed from their student role and identity, and were positioned as a colleague. She continues,

> I would say mostly like all my external blocks [rotations] were great. I don't have any complaints. They treat you as a coworker. They treat you as a peer. They let you do a lot of stuff. They ask your opinion on things. And that was really nice to be treated as an equal.

At times, students were reflective of the ways in which human dynamics—particularly of race, gender, and nationality, shaped their experiences in the teaching hospital. One of the few men in my study, Andrew, is candid in reflecting on how his identity made his experience in the hospital much easier,

> So, not to end on a negative note, but there are some serious cultural issues that are really frustrating. And I've been very lucky because I'm pretty easy to get along with and just not trying to—I'm pretty easy to get along with. I'm pretty smart. I can usually get by pretty well in clinics. I'm a guy, which helps a lot, especially with certain people, unfortunately. But I do think that's the case. So I've been very lucky.

Andrew went on to explain some of the concerns he had heard from his friends, whose experiences were not as easy,

> I've heard of on certain evals criticisms of people's accents, which is extremely inappropriate. . . . I've had friends—I have a friend who's on the spectrum with autism that has had a terrible experience the majority of this year with how she's been treated and how hard it's been to get people to really try to understand her situation and help her with it even when she's upfront. And she works her ass off in every rotation. She does and still gets crapped on for it. And that's very frustrating to me. And she's super smart too. Large animal hospital's on fire most of the time and people are outright verbally abused there somewhat frequently. I think it's gotten a little better recently but, I don't know, there's problems here.

While Andrew felt that his time in the hospital was significantly less traumatic than that of his friends and classmates, he still feels upset about many aspects of it,

> Yeah, so my ECC [Emergency Critical Care] evaluation, I didn't read the second one. I only read the first one. They said a lot of mean things about me, and then also said I should seriously reconsider pursuing emergency medicine, which was very hurtful, but it was also very frustrating because I actually did very well on that block and got along really well with one of the critical residents and was her guy, to some extent, on a lot of things. But the person who wrote the eval did not like me. At least that's what I assume happened. . . . And even the worst thing was probably being told I shouldn't do ER after telling them I want to do ER on the ER rotation where I worked my ass off and felt like I actually did a really good job.

Students' emotions during these meetings were often raw, painful, and unfiltered, as these reflections make clear. Students felt free to share these negative experiences with me for multiple reasons. First, our conversations occurred within weeks, or in some cases, days, of graduation. Students had passed their veterinary boards, secured employment, and knew that they were on a path to leaving veterinary school behind. They no longer feared the veterinary school, and for many of them, it was evident that they no longer had respect for the institution, either. Second, these were my fifth interviews with students. By this point, they knew me and had been sharing personal stories with me for many years. Of course, during our first meeting in 2015, I told them explicitly about Institutional Review Board (IRB) rules and regulations regarding confidentiality, and they had been presented with all required approvals and documents. While this meeting was long forgotten, students knew that their previous stories were confidential: they had not been called into the Dean's Office to discuss a remark that they made to me, so they now felt assured that anything they told me was private. Several students, not realizing that the study was concluding as they graduated, asked me how we were going to meet the following year—would we be using Zoom?

I share these stories from students' final year at the beginning because their own personal emotional states shape the remainder of the chapter. At this juncture in their veterinary education, students realize the central importance of human and human stories to veterinary medicine, including themselves, their colleagues and co-workers, and the human owners and clients whom they interact with daily. The stories they tell of stress, anxiety, and sheer exhaustion are not connected to or involved with animals: animals fade into the background as human pain, trauma, and distress become the central experiences of their lives.

IT'S ABOUT HUMANS: LEARNING FROM CLIENTS

As the stories discussed thus far in this chapter suggest, it is human interactions, stress, and conflict that dominate students' realities during their clinical rotations. During their rotations at the teaching hospital, students have their first experiences working with clients, particularly in the small animal setting, where they are generally the primary liaison between the client and the team at the hospital who is caring for the animal patient. As Alex reflected in the previous section, often this is a very difficult position for students, because they are the primary contact with the client even though they are powerless within the hospital system. As a result, a client will be pressuring and pushing a student for quick diagnostics, treatments and updates about their pet or animal, but the student is unable to do anything.

Amidst all this pressure, students begin to realize that they need to listen to and understand the client, because they do not have feelings of attachment for every animal that they see. This is a critical lesson for students as they begin to realize the limits of the veterinary profession as a place where one solely loves animals. Instead, they confront an institutional and professional *human* system in which animals are not always central to the dynamics that are unfolding. Christina reflects on her struggles with empathizing with her human clients,

> Part of that is something I've been working on is empathy. Because I feel like sometimes that's hard for me because I am not as attached to a pet as someone else. And I'm

like, "Okay. Your dog has this horrendous thing going on. Euthanasia's probably the best option." Which we present, obviously, a little bit nicer way and do give them all of the options if they want to buy the next two weeks or whatever it may be. But I feel like sometimes that's been hard for me when it's someone who's so emotional. Because I just met this pet for the first time, but they've known them for 10-plus years. So that's definitely something I'll have to get used to and I feel like depending on who the person is, if I can relate to them on a personal level, just their lifestyle, if they remind me of someone I'm really close with or something I feel like it's a little bit easier.

For many of the students, like Christina, they realize that they need to be able to relate to and understand the human to be able to help the animal: there is no innate, emotional attachment to the pet, once they have seen hundreds of pets facing illness, disease, and potential euthanasia. Michelle explains this in detail, reflecting on her rotations in the large animal hospital as she discusses how she tries to match (or mirror) the owner's relationship with the animal,

> We adapt to what the owner feels like. I don't know what it is. It's just I feel like when you know how bonded the owner is to the animal, it doesn't affect how you care for that animal, but I think it affects—like for a cow, you're not going to go in and wash its face every day, but with a potbelly pig who's used to getting its face washed every day, you might take that extra time to do that and—I don't know—just kind of matching what that owner might be doing for that animal. I think it just kind of—I think your bond kind of changes patient to patient based on kind of what the owner seems—like how they seem to be bonded with the animal, if that makes sense. I don't know. That's kind of what I've been noticing, and not just me. I've kind of talked to other people [in the large animal hospital] about this horse that I kind of ended up really liking, and I was like, "Man. I really don't like horses, but I really like this one horse," and they kind of said the same thing. When the owner seems to really care about the animal, they [the veterinarians in the hospital] care more about the animal. And when they don't seem to really care about the animal at all, of course, they still treat it the same, but they don't feel as much of an attachment, I guess.

Like many of the students, Andrew's experiences with clients are mixed: some pleasant, some exceedingly stressful. Yet, he finds a space for himself, and his voice and position as a doctor as he helps a client understand how to help their elderly dog with heart disease. As Andrew explains, the attending cardiologist had met with the client, but the veterinarian's explanation was complex, and the client, whose dog was in crisis, was having difficulty making sense of the recommendations and options available,

> That is one of my favorite things of the job is communicating with people and helping them understand what's going on. And I feel like I've done that pretty well throughout this year, just kind of sitting with people and explaining why we're doing what we're doing. . . . I got really frustrated on my cardiology rotation because I felt like there was a big disconnect between some of the doctors within the cardiology department and clients. . . . So one thing that sticks out to me is this wasn't helping someone in crisis. I remember there is this one lady who brought in this older Whippet that had pretty significant heart disease, like had been in heart failure and was managing heart failure.

I remember the doctor drew this diagram of the heart and went through the physiology of the disease that was happening and all that stuff, and I could see the client's
eyes glaze over. . . . I could just tell they're upset, they're overwhelmed, they don't
know what to do, they don't really understand what's going on. So after that doctor
left, I sat down with them and spent just 10 or 15 minutes somewhat re-explaining that
I like much simpler terms like, "Here's what's happening." And then kind of talk to
her and say like, "Listen, eventually, this is going to be it. The good news is here are
the things that we can do to prolong a good quality of life and give you good time with
your pet." I just kind of told her, "We don't have to euthanize your dog yet, which is
excellent. And it's okay that eventually, we're going to have to. That doesn't mean what
we're doing is futile. The goal is for you to enjoy this time. The end goal of this is not
to get as many years as possible, it's just for you to have this time together. At the end,
you've given this dog an excellent life for all of these years. That's great. You haven't
done anything wrong." And then just talking to her like that, I could see her just visibly
again—and maybe just she was relieved, much more relaxed, much more comfortable
with what we talked about on the discharge.

But for some students, talking with clients is overwhelming. The one international
student in my study, Lin, struggles to relate to U.S. clients, as she tells me,

But every day, if I have 20 cases, and then the owners, some of them are really easy
to deal with, but some of them are really difficult. And the difficult ones sometimes
make my day really terrible. Some of them—maybe because my background is not
from here, so they give me a lot of information that I don't think is necessary and don't
know how to process.

Sometimes they will describe it, and that's like from movies, and they will say
"That scene, you remember?" and "It's like my dog in there." I was like, "I have no clue
what that scene is," and then I don't know how to react. And sometimes, I feel really
awkward there, but I don't want to make it awkward. And I try to say something and
I make it even more awkward.

I don't know if I can use this word in talking the interview because I feel some of
them are racist. And then I do feel like as a foreigner—I guess they can feel that I have
an accent, and that I have a different face, and then they don't trust me as much.

Earlier in the year, clients at the teaching hospital had filed a complaint about her and
she had been through a trying few months as that situation unfolded. With a mixture
of reluctance and relief, Lin had decided to follow her interest in imaging, and has
accepted an internship in another teaching hospital for the following year. She told
me she is looking forward to sitting in a dark room all day, looking at and interpreting images, instead of interacting with clients. While she still wants to work directly
with animals, this past year has been a revelation, as she tells me, "After fourth year,
after what I've been through the last year it (veterinary medicine) is actually getting
the information to the human."

ADJUSTMENT, RESISTANCE, AND RENEWAL

Students in my study find multiple ways to cope with the overwhelming pressure
that they face during this final trial before they graduate, are fully licensed, and

can finally leave. Students take three overarching approaches to coping: they adjust, either through actively changing their approach or resignation; they resist in small and subtle ways; and they find spaces of renewal, through connecting back to the animal patients whom they have lost in this process.

For some, it was a relatively simple process of adjusting to a new reality. Allison's process of adjusting to uncertainty was hard, but straightforward,

> I personally find it (fourth year) harder. Because we're in the classroom setting our whole lives up to now, so you get very used to being in a classroom a lot. So when you think of it, you're in the classroom, there's a lecture, there's PowerPoint, there's notes or whatever. But you know you're going to be tested on that material. There's a lot of certainty about it, even if you don't know what they're going to ask, you know the general frame of what they're going to ask. When you're in clinics you could be asked anything, anything could happen, anything could walk in the door. So there's a lot less certainty. I think for me that took a little bit of getting used to because you're just so used to having a good idea of what's going to happen. And then you go again to clinics, and it's like anything could happen.

Lin, the international student who I discussed earlier, finds some comfort in the routine of her daily life, even though she has little control over it,

> My life is basically, the night before, I see these cases, go home, read all this case history, figure out what this patient will need, go to school, see the clients, talk to them, extract as much as useful information that we'll need for the patient since the last visit. And then, use that information, process it, go through my diagnosis, talk to the adults, the clinicians, what my plans are. Figure out what would the best for the patients and financial-wise, for the clients, and then present them to them. Sometimes they're happy, sometimes they're angry. And then, just get through that emotional ride from the patients and the owner. And then, treat the patient, write all my case report, go home, eat, sleep, and start over again. So that's how my fourth year seems to be.

Brandon and Heather both specifically discussed how the relentless pace and unforgiving atmosphere of the veterinary hospital had led them away from their original reason for entering the profession, their connection to animals. Brandon tells me,

> I just think it does kind of desensitize you to—I'm not as interested in the animal as I am in getting my treatments done because I'm just trying to keep my head above water. I have to get the rounds, but I have to get these treatments done before eight. So I don't know. I think it's not—it doesn't really help. I think vet school didn't really help my relationship with animals, which is ironic.

Heather has a similar reflection,

> I just I feel like it contributes to just becoming numb to everything and caring less and that's really unfortunate because that's why we got into this profession. I haven't even started my actual job yet and I feel a little emotionally blunted from trying to ignore these things that the techs are doing and these various things that I've seen.

Heather continues and describes in detail an incident she witnessed as a dog was being euthanized in the veterinary hospital. In her reflection, she discusses the yellow binder. As she explains it, veterinary students at CMU must complete this binder—which includes a series of procedures, tasks, and observations—in order to graduate,

> I think the yellow binder has made some people a little bit more numb about their patients. Two weeks ago there was a dog that was being euthanized in the ER and word had gotten out that the client agreed that it could be used for yellow binder purposes. I'm not quite sure how they explained that to the client but there were people literally waiting outside the door while this dog was still alive and being euthanized with its family that were waiting to practice things on it to get their yellow binder stuff signed off. And to me, that's—yes. You have to get your yellow binder done but to be waiting there before the dog's even euthanized, that is emotional burnout to me. Because you're not thinking this is the dog's last moments. You're just waiting for it to be dead so you can practice drawing blood or you know and that's so sad.

One of the ways that students adjusted and coped with the pressure was to accept that it was part of the profession even if they did not agree with the practice. Heather refers to what she experienced as "hazing" and comments that, "I mean, you hear stories from all of medicine how this is how it's always been done, you have to pay your dues. And it shouldn't be that way."

Marissa tells me how she developed anxiety for the first time during veterinary school, but that she feels that this is normal for the profession,

> I definitely developed anxiety in veterinary school. And I've never experienced it prior. I can't recall, even in undergraduate, having it so I think it's alarming. . . . But it helps to know that we're all feeling that. My roommates feel like that. The doctors, they're very poised but if you're very close with them, they'll open up with you and tell you like, "Yeah, I had anxiety too." And I almost wonder if it's always been happening in our profession, and it's just been so taboo that no one's been talking about it.

RESISTANCE AND RENEWAL: RECONNECTING TO THE WORLD

Students in my study rarely, if ever, had an opportunity to resist any part of the curriculum of veterinary school. However, they still find small spaces and opportunities to assert their independence from the veterinary school. Through doing this, they challenge the professionalism that they are expected to accept and inhabit, instead using their lay or humanistic perspective to navigate everyday experiences (Goldberg, 2008). While of course Goldberg's research focuses on the human medical profession, the parallels to the veterinary profession are striking.

One of the small though constant ways that student resisted is that they learned to simple disregard the opinions and perspectives of faculty. Many of the students tell me that after the first few clinical rotations, they no longer read their evaluations because they no longer cared what their supervisors thought of them. They began to look inside themselves for validation, instead of to the institution of the veterinary school. As I discussed in Chapter 5, Christina deliberately rejected the veterinary school's strong request that she not use her vacation block for an additional experience with the Rural Area Veterinary Services. But examples such as Christina's are rare. Students succumb to the demands even as they complain because they have little choice if they want to become licensed veterinarians: they are entering a profession governed by rules, procedures, and absolutes, and they have learned to follow them.

Thus, Marissa's approach is poignant and touching as she resists in tiny ways that are, nonetheless, significant to her. Throughout my interviews with Marissa over the years, she consistently talks about feeling an emotional "energy" with animals, which I first discussed in Chapter 3. She explains it me, again, during our final interview, "I think that emotional connection, that energy thing, has always been with me, maybe it's a gift. So I've learned to read it more, especially with my gut, as well." She goes on how to tell me she uses this energy to read and feel a situation when she is exhausted, such as on emergency rotations,

> I keep referring to emergency, but I just saw so many cases. I'd say like 70 cases in three weeks. So, on emergency, that helped out a lot. I think early mornings, late nights, whatever you want to call it, when you have to depend on that. Sometimes I may not be as sharp as I can be, so but just feeling that energy, I'm like, "Okay, something needs my attention here." I need to figure out why or how, either from the owner, like their uneasiness or from the pet, as well.

When I ask Marissa, several times over the years, whether she had talked with her veterinary colleagues about this "energy" she said yes sometimes, but that they just said the equivalent of, "we all have that." Yet clearly Marissa feels that she has something different that most veterinarians are not aware of within themselves or are not perhaps interested in exploring. While Marissa's senses are not validated by her immediate colleagues, as Ware (2018) has indicated, the idea that (at least some) veterinary professionals interact with an animal's spirit, soul, or essence, is a strong, if sometimes ignored or sublimated, current in the field.

Marissa uses her sense of "energy" as a way to connect to clients and in this sense, she resists, outwardly if quietly accepted practices in the veterinary profession,

> I don't know if it's because [central Midwest state] is conservative compared to where I grew up. But we're told, like, "Don't touch the client, don't hug the client, don't cry in front of clients." And I think all that's bogus. I hug clients, I hug them here, I hug them back home when I was seeing appointments on my off-campus rotations.
>
> I had a dog with really bad neck pain, and it winded up being bone cancer. So again, another situation that unfortunately, we had to humanely euthanize him. The client had the dog, he was a Springer Spaniel. So maybe 40 pounds on his lap. And the other client was holding my hand. She's like, "Can I hold your hand?" I'm like, "Absolutely." It's almost like she felt from the clinician that was in the room with me, was maybe more stoic. And I get it. She had the euthanasia solution in her hand. But I was holding her [the client's] hand, I was rubbing her back, she hugged me, or she embraced me. I think all that's fine. I just don't I don't know why it's taboo here. And again, I don't know if it's just culture and things like that, but I am very against it. I don't have strong opinions about many things, but that's one thing I don't think is appropriate.

Even though Marissa uses the word "client" as she describes her experience, she also resists that language, telling me, "So we're told client care. It's your clients, blah, blah, blah, but I call it mom and dad. I do that all the time." For Marissa, this shift in language, though small, is significant, because it refocuses the attention on the relationship and connection between the owner/parent/guardian and the patient/animal, mirroring the pediatrician approach to the veterinary profession, and simultaneously directly contradicting and resisting what she has been expressly told is acceptable professional conduct.

Other students do not outwardly resist, but they find spaces in which they can renew their commitment to their chosen path through connecting back to what they had originally assumed was the core of the profession: animals. These connections directly to animals always happen when clients are not present, but when students are alone with animal patients, with perhaps one other student. Generally the animal is extremely sick or close to death, and the student is the one tasked with the job of comfort and nursing care. Sometimes, students are intimately involved in euthanasia, particularly if the client has chosen not to be present. Jennifer describes a touching, emotional moment with a dog patient who was euthanized without the client,

> They (the clients) lived at least a couple hours away, and they just wanted us to euthanize him, and they didn't want to come for it, which was very hard, personally, because I would want to be there with my pet. I know everyone handles that differently. I mean, I don't know. I wasn't there when he came in at ECC. Maybe they kind of thought something bad was going to happen, so they did byes the night before—I don't know— but it was just really hard for them to be like, "Go ahead" and give the okay to euthanize him over the phone and not be there, and the way that we handle that in hospitals, you have to have a witness to whoever you're on the phone with, so my clinician was on the phone with them, and then so he put it on speakerphone, and I had to be the witness so I could hear that, and the guy sounded upset, but he didn't come.
>
> We sat with the dog in ICU for probably an hour or so and tried to get him to eat some food and stuff. And I mean, we were going to euthanize him anyway, so we were just trying to feed him anything that he would eat. So we brought M&Ms in and potato chips and all kinds of things just to try to make his last time there a little bit better, but he didn't really want to eat anything, unfortunately, but we tried because we just felt so bad.

As Jennifer talked, I pictured her on the floor with an extremely sick dog in her lap, trying to feed him candy and potato chips and comfort him through his final moments. As a student, she would not be the one to administer the "blue juice" (Morris, 2012)—that reality was still a few months in the future. But as she sat, and I am sure cried a little, she escaped the bounds of the teaching hospital and the larger profession. People who are religious often imagine dogs running free in heaven: such images are common on pet remembrance sites such as the very popular Rainbow Bridge. While Jennifer was very much alive, I like to imagine that being with that dog in his final moments allowed her to run a little freer in this life, in this world, and to rediscover her own humanity within a system that tries to deny it.

THE OATH: FINALLY BECOMING A VETERINARIAN

Being admitted to the profession of veterinary medicine, I solemnly swear to use my scientific knowledge and skills for the benefit of society through the protection of animal health and welfare, the prevention and relief of animal suffering, the conservation of animal resources, the promotion of public health, and the advancement of medical knowledge.

I will practice my profession conscientiously, with dignity, and in keeping with the principles of veterinary medical ethics.

I accept as a lifelong obligation the continual improvement of my professional knowledge and competence.

As I discussed in Chapter 5, veterinary students at CMU say the veterinary oath together as a group for the first time at their white coat ceremony. At that moment, they are on the cusp of their fourth year of veterinary school, directly before they begin clinical rotations and interacting with patients and clients in a "becoming veterinarian" role. Now, at the end of their fourth year of veterinary school, they recite it again as they graduate, a ceremonial transition that is rapidly approaching. This time when they recite the oath, it represents the actual moment of taking responsibility for being a veterinarian and figuring out what meaning the oath has for them as a person and as a professional.

Through my years of talking to and meeting with the students, we focused on the various aspects of the oath. As I told them during our first meeting as they were entering veterinary school, I was particularly interested in animal welfare as that was a recent (2011) addition to the oath. Until that time, the U.S. veterinarian's oath included a commitment to "animal health" only, consistent with the history of the veterinary profession and its focus on serving the human client first, with consideration for the animal patient only understood within the needs and desire of the client/owner (Bones & Yeates, 2012; Jones, 2003). While there was considerable opposition within the profession at the time (Nolen, 2011), "animal welfare" is now increasingly accepted as a key component of the practice of veterinary medicine. The addition of "animal welfare" broadens the scope of concern for the animal patient but retains a paradigm that places human needs and desires at the center (American Veterinary Medical Association, 2021b).

Now, during our final interviews, I give them a copy of the oath, ask them to read it, and then to talk with me about what it means to them as they graduate, take the oath, and move into the veterinary profession. Marissa is very excited as I hand it to her and she reads it to herself, "My heart's pounding. I guess because we get—we recite this after we graduate too. . . . I can't wait to recite this."

Several of the students saw the oath as just basic commonsense, providing reasonable guidance to them as new veterinarians. Andrew told me,

So it's not like our—when I read the oath, it's not like, "Oh, gosh. I'm not going to do that," or "Oh, gosh. Like how crazy that they expect me to do X, Y or Z." It's more like, "Yeah. That's pretty much like how I'd like to do things, so that's good." I don't know. I mean, I'd want to practice conscientiously with dignity and ethically. So I don't have any intention of not doing that, so I don't. It doesn't rouse strong emotions to think about that because I guess that's what I want to do, and obviously, the conversation that we've been having—it's very much an ethical minefield, so maybe I should be more worried. But I also like—at the end of the day, I just have to do what I can, do what I think is best and learn from the times I make mistakes, and that's all I can do, so.

Allison also interprets the oath as a general reminder to try to have good ethics, work to the best of her ability and to help people and animals,

> I guess I see it as kind of like our promise to essentially kind of—I see it as kind of a way to work for the better good and promise that we're going to have good intentions and do things to practice to the top standard that we can, that kind of thing, and follow good ethical and just have good ethics and stuff like that. And to really kind of—because veterinarians have a pretty good reputation, I think. And so it's kind of keeping that reputation and trying to just kind of essentially be good people. Do things to the best of our ability and use it to help animals and humans. It seems like recently, especially, there's been a real push for kind of bringing together human medicine and vet medicine to help with public health and stuff like that. And so kind of keeping that in mind and having good practices with your antibiotic use and kind of keeping both the humans and animals in mind. And just kind of—I don't know. I guess, I just haven't formulated an exact answer for that, but. Those are kind of some of my random thoughts that pop into my head. But, yeah. So just kind of—yeah. That's pretty much it. I don't have too much to add right now.

The part of the oath that focuses on the prevention of animal suffering resonated for many students after their rotations in the teaching hospital, where they were constantly faced with animals whose suffering could only be relieved through euthanasia. Heather comments, "The prevention and relief of animal suffering definitely from the euthanasia perspective. That's huge to me, the relieving of suffering." Many students relate stories of animals in the teaching hospitals who had to wait too long for pain relief, and how this had disturbed them. For example, Erin recollects,

> I know a classmate who's on the ER right now, and she said there was an animal that was sitting without pain meds and she felt it really needed pain meds. And it was just sitting while the doctors kind of put over the case for whatever, trying to figure out what they wanted to do. And she's like, "I really just wanted to start pain meds on this animal." And then she asked, because the doctor who was working with her wouldn't really listen to her, so she went to the doctor above that doctor and got pain meds. But then the doctor that was working with her kind of was not the happiest about it because she kind of went over her head. So there was a little drama there, but at the end of the day, at least the animal got started on something so. It was like she was looking out for her animal even though she kind of got reprimanded a little bit.
>
> I've had to be quite insistent about that here, about that needs to happen immediately. And I understand you need to evaluate, but this also has to happen immediately, pain meds.

For these students, their experiences in the teaching hospital helped them see that the veterinary oath had practical implications and that "prevention of animal suffering" in addition to multiple aspects of the oath, has varying interpretations. This was also true for several who were beginning to see the inherent conflicts in the veterinary oath, as they were simultaneously tasked with helping and harming animals. For example, I had a long conversation with Kiara, the student who had previously worked at the USDA facility involved in the kitten experiments that had since been stopped. As she began her required four years with the USDA, Kiara was looking forward to a career as a regulatory veterinarian. However, until I explicitly asked her, she had not given much thought to the reality that she was going to be the one charged with regulating animal welfare. In response to that aspect of the oath, she comments,

> I mean, it's important because, I mean, as a regulatory veterinarian, that's something that we regulate, is the animal welfare [laughter]. So it's very important. . . . I was like, "Wow. Dang." But yeah, it is—yeah, I mean, that's it, really [laughter]. It's super-important because that is basically what we are dealing with.

Kiara's laughter reflects, I believe, that she was nervous. Though we were discussing a serious subject that was immediately relevant to her future, and would become a reality in just a few months, she had not fully considered what it meant for her. Our conversation then turned back to her thoughts about what she had witnessed at the USDA facility a few years earlier. She tells me,

> I feel like my stance is still similar in regards to—not what I'm doing. *I'm not injecting these kittens* (my emphasis)—but what is being done isn't just happening for the fun of it. It's for a purpose to learn more about the disease and in general—if it relates to animal health, which I mean toxoplasmosis does—to get to the bottom of it. And I think it's really difficult to do that or to figure out scientific discoveries without using what needs to be used. So I mean, I feel like me personally when I was there, they're treated with the best care—despite them not feeling well they get treated with the utmost care, and they don't prolong their suffering longer than it needs to. So I don't know.

In this case, there was no one in the institution to absolve (Arluke & Hafferty, 1996) Kiara of responsibility. Thus, she absolved herself through her stance that she was not responsible, as she was not the one doing the injections. Kiara's ability to compartmentalize and divide herself from the suffering she saw right in front of her also extends to students' relationships with other students, whose veterinary paths were taking them in different directions. Jessica struggles with the love and connection she felt to her roommate, who was going into pig production, and thus contributing to the continuation of an industry that Jessica found disturbing. She tells me,

> all of the suffering that goes into the production of meat. I think that it's getting better and they're caring more about the animal psychological wellbeing, but there's still a lot to be desired in that area. And I think if I thought about it every day, I would maybe be less inclined to eat meat. But I think the fact that I put it out in my mind, I don't think about it, but it's really sad what happens in that industry. My roommate is going into pig medicine. And when I hear stories about her from work, I am horrified. Or just the things that she sees, I'm horrified. But then I think I just compartmentalize it and

I don't think about it. . . . And it kind of disturbs me that it's not (horrifying) to her. But then I think I again, just try to compartmentalize it. Because I love her as a person. I don't want to think of her as somebody who doesn't care about animals.

Christina also explores areas of conflict in how "animal welfare" and "animal suffering" are differentially applied in the veterinary field. In the end, she relies on the fact that the profession accepts this difference and is ultimately simply following public demand,

> So it's very weird, but I still feel, I think, the same way, that I think the biggest issue is just perception. Sometimes I think yes, we have workers at these places that maybe could go about things differently. But overall, the animals are well cared for. Their basic needs are met, and I think it's a perception thing because we have pets—it's hard for people who haven't grown up with livestock or production animals to make that distinction between production and pet, but then they still are like, "Well, I still eat hamburger, and I still eat chicken, and I still want all this stuff, but I want them to have 10-foot rooms each and be pet every night and sung to sleep." That's just unrealistic to feed the population. So I'd still think that that's a big concern.

These students implicitly recognized the segmented collective identity (Vermilya, 2015) that is inherent in the veterinary profession, and that while the oath is an umbrella for the entire profession, how it is interpreted and used in practice varies dramatically. Their veterinary education exposed them to this reality, leaving these contradictions and challenges largely unexplored. For example, the veterinary profession accepts that the assessment of "animal suffering" and "animal welfare" will be different depending on whether that animal is a pet or destined for slaughter. As a result, students come to believe that this is normal and natural: simply the way that the world and the profession operate. In this sense, their veterinary education has prepared them well to be "mechanics," but they are left without the ability to raise critical questions and to contribute to the development of veterinary medical ethics (Linzey & Linzey, 2017; Morris, 2012; Richards et al., 2020; Rollin, 2019).

At the same time, students also understand at an innate level that the words contained in the oath are important aspects of veterinary medicine, and that their professional obligation is real and lifelong. This past year has taught them that—they have all witnessed countless cases of animal suffering. They know, at last, that what they are planning to do is not something imagined and hoped for, but a soon to be lived reality. Erin tells me,

> You're always going to think about these cases. You're going to reflect on them. You're going to wonder if you made the right decision of if you said the right thing. So that's a realization that I've come to, as well, is that you're going to carry a lot of these. And I think it's possible to carry guilt or sadness or things like that even when the situation's been over with for a while. So it's definitely a commitment.

Lin is very reflective, in these final weeks and moments of her student life, of the obligation that is looming,

> To me, the last sentence [of the oath] is very heavy. . . . This is a lifelong thing. . . .
> I know there are vets out there that work for several years. And then for females,
> somehow they become just a housewife, and they don't do this anymore. But yeah, so
> for them, probably it's not going to be lifelong. If you don't keep working on this, you
> lose your license, and they somehow decide to sacrifice that and becoming a house-
> wife. And for me, sometimes I'm really tired. It's like, "Oh my God. I have to do this
> lifelong," and then "Can I handle this?"

While Lin is actively struggling with the implications of the veterinary oath for her
life, there are some students who simply are too overwhelmed with emotion and
exhaustion to even begin to discuss it with me. These are the students—and there
were several—who broke down in tears during our meeting. They could not continue
talking at points, and expressed overwhelming sadness, anger, and disappointment.[2]
Brianna was one of these students. In our conversation, I talk, but Brianna has nothing to say.

> **Nadine:** I wanted to ask you about—I've been asking everybody. So this is the
>   veterinary oath. And I just wanted to get a sense of what this means to you
>   as you finish your DVM and go into your future, which, for you, it looks
>   like it could go in different directions. What pieces are important to you?
>   What's going to be shaping you?
> [silence]
> **Brianna:** I don't know.
> [silence]
> **Brianna:** Yeah. I don't know how to answer that.

ENDINGS ALWAYS LEAD SOMEWHERE: MOVING FORWARD

The stories that students tell me about their fourth and final year of veterinary school
were often painful, and sometimes excruciating. It was particularly challenging
for the students in my study to face this reality because it was not what they had
expected. They had certainly heard from upper-class students that fourth year was
hard, but details were vague. Going into their clinical rotations, my participants were
happy to finally be completely done with the classroom, to don their white coats, and
to step into the space of transitional liminality on their way to graduation. The anticipation of the end of the journey prevented them from fully being able to prepare for
the hardships they were about to encounter.

Perhaps there is no way to adequately prepare for their clinical rotations. The
constant stress and exhaustion that is inherent in the profession, the lack of concentrated attention on the central ethical and moral issues that are ever-present, and the
sharp internal contradictions that govern everyday practices suggest that students
are entering a profession that itself has lost its center. The students in my study confront these issues on a daily basis, but with little to no guidance. Deeply engulfed
in the "mechanic" model of veterinary education, there were no opportunities to
discuss, reflect, or even argue about the very real and constant tensions, pressures,

and crosscurrents that face the veterinary profession today in the context of changing scientific research and new societal norms and values regarding animals.

In the next chapter, I explore some of these emergent new worlds, connecting the stories of my students to the contemporary societal transformations that surround veterinary education and the profession.

NOTES

1 After a pet is euthanized, many veterinary practices and hospitals offer the client a clay paw imprint of their pet as a keepsake and remembrance.

2 As a researcher, I have an ethical responsibility to the students in my study. Over the years, numerous students cried. I often stopped the interview if the students wanted me to leave the room so that they could have some privacy before continuing. These emotions, fueled by stress and exhaustion, were exceptionally strong during these final interviews. I used many tissues and had to pause several interviews. There was one student during these final interviews whom I was particularly concerned about and felt uncomfortable with her leaving the room given her emotional state. After the formal interview was over, we chatted for a while, I asked her about her plans for the rest of the day and made sure she had people to talk with before she left. I delve further into my experience of interviewing in Chapter 9.

7 Telling New Stories
Toward Different Animal and Human Futures

These are just things I haven't said out loud. Nobody asked me these questions. Because I am passionate about it and I think that is why I'm crying because I do love it. Although it's hard, I would do it all over again because I love it.

—Anna, final interview

We must accept the fact that love for animals can augment veterinary science rather than hinder it, and that love should no longer be devalued in the profession. The world cannot get too much of this precious commodity as the damaged planet cries out for gentle programs of healing and renewal.

Lawrence (1994, p. 972)

Anna cried profusely in our final conversation together. She cried for her love of the veterinary profession and for her love of animals. But as she reflects, she also cries because in her four years of veterinary education, no one has ever asked her these questions, except for me.

Through my four years and hundreds of hours of interviews, I heard many stories that made me feel angry, disappointed, despondent, and sometimes hopeless: stories of how animals were mistreated, how humans struggled to simply survive intact psychologically to the next day. But no story I heard in four years made me feel sadder than Anna's, because through her tears she told me that there was no space, no room, no invitation in her four years of veterinary education to discuss love. She had entered the veterinary profession precisely because of that love, but when she arrived, she discovered it was not valued. No one, except me, had time or interest in this unabiding, all-encompassing love that she felt.

Now, of course, it is possible that other students felt their love for the profession and for animals validated at some point. However, considering the overwhelming intensity and negativity of my final interviews with the students, I suspect it was rare. Though I asked and probed, there was very little response. My conclusion may simply be an artifact of interviewing students at a moment when they were particularly emotionally vulnerable, exhausted, and depleted. But the larger picture of veterinary education and the veterinary profession suggests that there is a truth here, even if partial, and that Anna's painful reflection indexes a hidden reality. Love—for animals and for people—is devalued, as Lawrence's epigraph at the beginning of this chapter suggests. Love is buried and often suffocated in the field. The evidence of this is

DOI: 10.1201/9781003269984-7

everywhere: particularly striking are the high suicide rates among both students and the profession overall (Tomasi et al., 2019). Marissa's comment in Chapter 6 that she developed anxiety for the first time in veterinary school yet has come to accept it as normal within the profession is a startling admission. She has rationalized to herself that if she is going to be a veterinarian, she needs to accept that mental health problems, including her present anxiety, will be an ongoing reality for her. What additional mental health issues will she develop over her career and simply, again, accept as "normal"?

In this chapter, I begin a discussion of the possibilities of telling new stories about animals and humans in veterinary medicine, where "love"—in all its entangled complexity, is at the center. Throughout, I use excerpts from my years of interviews with the students where their voices and experience point to hope and to new directions. I explore these emergent possibilities both within and outside of the field of veterinary medicine, bringing the profession into productive conversation with contemporary developments in fields such as medical and veterinary humanities, education, and cognitive ethology. These new developments point to a future where Anna can express her love without fear, Marissa can understand that anxiety is not simply part of the profession, and where, in the end, the animal is who matters.

ON LOVE AND SCIENTISM IN VETERINARY MEDICINE

As Anna's quote—the opening epigraph for this chapter—suggests, the concept of "love" is at the core of understanding how to remake and rethink the veterinary profession. For Anna and many other students who participated in this study, love was perhaps tacitly assumed to be present, though difficult to see and experience and never openly discussed. Was love an undercurrent in their daily lives in veterinary school? For the students in my study, the answer was generally no. Love, specifically love for animals, was experienced in private spaces with their own animals or those of their classmates. But in the professional spaces of the veterinary school, love was rarely discussed. Perhaps because love was assumed to be present, there was a tacit agreement that discussion was unnecessary. Perhaps there was simply no time to discuss or engage in conversations about "soft" subjects such as love, when there was a demanding science-based curriculum to master. Perhaps conversations about love are too challenging for a profession that is mired in the eternal contradiction of professing to be concerned for animals' health and welfare, at the same time that it intertwined with industries that cause immeasurable animal suffering and pain, such as the laboratory animal research, horse racing, captive animal entertainment (e.g., zoos and aquariums), and the entire "food" animal industry (see Waldau, 2007). As a result of the multiple, separate paths that veterinary students take, the segmented collective identity that Vermilya (2015) identifies likely also plays a role in the missing conversations about love. "Love" of animals looks very different across species in a veterinary environment. Students following a small animal track are expected to have a different relationship with the animals in their care than students in a "food" animal track. I use the phrase "in a veterinary environment" quite deliberately, because as I will discuss later in this chapter, there is no biological need to differentiate these loves: quite the contrary, a person can love a dog, a pig, a cow, and a turtle in the same way. But the veterinary profession draws bright, hard lines between the species: lines which humans cross daily, that science continues to erode, and that society questions in an increasingly loud and demanding voice. Thus, while society may assume that veterinarians love animals, as evidenced by the messages sent through children's books, the view from inside the profession is profoundly different.

Almost 30 years ago, Lawrence (1994) addressed the reality of love in the veterinary profession in one of the only articles authored by a veterinarian published on the topic in the official journals of the veterinary field. The majority of articles in the professional journals that address the topic of love do so through a discussion of the human–animal bond, in the context of client-owned animals in small animal medicine. Articles that look at the complicated relationship between veterinarians themselves and animals are rare (Manette, 2004; Martinsen & Jukes, 2005; Waldau, 2007). As I do in this book, Lawrence notes that while love of animals is assumed by the public to be a necessary trait of veterinarians and thus a defining precept for the field, within veterinary medicine love is either ignored or dismissed. As Lawrence discusses, in veterinary medicine, as in other "scientific" fields, love is assumed to be counter to "science." Lawrence traces this separation back to Cartesian dualism and the Eurocentric belief in the separation of rationality from feeling, from emotions and the body. There is an abiding misbelief, as I have commented on previously, that "Reason, not emotion, is what makes us human" (Dolby, 2012, p. 54). It is important to note, as Lawrence and I both do, that this fundamental dichotomy between reason and emotion stems not from science, but from philosophy: the dualism of heart and mind rests in Descartes, and it then was propagated and reinforced by Eurocentric science. Thus, in veterinary medicine the epitome of being a "good" veterinarian is to be a scientist, which in the story that is told in the profession and many others, means putting aside feelings, as if they can somehow be separated out and put into a shoebox under the bed. As an example, Lawrence writes about the formation of a new veterinary association focused on wildlife medicine and notes that the call for members included the specific directive that those without a "sentimental" interest in wildlife were welcome (1994, p. 970).

The idealization of a human-free, value-free, and completely objective science is what educational scholars and researchers Erickson and Gutierrez (2002), among others in many academic fields, refer to as "scientism," which reduces science to a series of steps that are universal, and might in fact, be equally well performed by a human and a robot. While scientism is endemic throughout the academy, including in my own field of education, Mccomas (1997) discusses the historical context of how the myth of the lockstep "scientific method" developed.

> The notion of a single scientific method is so pervasive that many students must be disappointed when they discover that scientists do not have a framed copy of the steps of the scientific method posted above each laboratory workbench.
>
> Close inspection will reveal that scientists approach and solve problems by using imagination, creativity, prior knowledge, and perseverance. These, of course, are the same methods used by all effective problem-solvers. The lesson to be learned is that science is no different from other human endeavors where puzzles are investigated.

(n.p.)

As McComas insists, the human is always present and part of science: the individual's particular imagination, creativity, life experiences, and multiple forms of subjec-
tivity are intrinsic parts of the story: they cannot be separated from the daily practice
of science. Davis and Sumara (2005) remind us that this is the ground for the actual,
historical development of "science" as a practice deeply embedded within human
context, perspectives, strengths, and frailties. Toulmin (1982) similarly reflects on
the changing understanding of the nature of science in light of Kuhn (1962), writing,

> As we now realize, the interaction between scientists and their objects of study is
> always a *two-way* affair. There is no way in which scientists can continue to reduce the
> effects of their observations on those objects without limit. . . . For natural scientists
> today, the classical posture of pure spectator is no longer available even on the level of
> pure theory.

(p. 97, emphasis is the author's)

As Ware (2018) notes, veterinarians are perhaps more invested in scientism because
of the continued devaluing of their profession, particularly in relationship to human
medicine. She writes, "Indeed, veterinarians may be even more wedded to con-
ventional scientific perspectives because their work is often misunderstood and
devalued as not 'real' medicine" (2018, p. 15). This is a phenomenon that is well
documented in fields such as the sociology of science and Science, Technology, and
Society (STS), where research shows that what science is and how it is practiced
is both variable and hierarchical (Knopes, 2019; Latour, 1987; Latour & Woolgar,
1979). In fields that garner less public respect, such as veterinary medicine, nursing, education, and many of the social sciences, the enforcement of strict, objective
procedures and protocols are critically enforced and policed as a way of producing
scientifically validated results to increase the standing of the profession. However,
in fields with higher public status, such as medicine and laboratory (bench) science,
these standards are relaxed, and science operates much more informally, through
conversations, consensus, and debate.

The remnants of Cartesian dualism and scientism persist in veterinary medicine.
It may be easier to simply avoid the many challenges that now exist to this worldview, as a reckoning with the questions of love, emotion, and the entanglements
of human–animal relationships is fundamentally further disruptive to the field of
veterinary medicine as a "science." For a field that has struggled to establish legitimacy and value in both opposition and cooperation with human medicine, change is
unwelcome. Yet, there is little doubt that both inside and outside of veterinary medicine, there are people and organizations that are attempting to move the field in a different direction, one that honors the emotional worlds of both humans and animals.

As much as the veterinary students in my study respect and value science, they
are aware that there is much more to their chosen profession than a rationality devoid
of emotion and connections to both animals and people. Even if they have never,
or rarely, had the opportunity to explore these feelings in their veterinary education, they know these connections are legitimate. For example, in our conversation
about the veterinary oath, Jessica specifically discusses her concerns about the sen-
tence that included the phrase "scientific knowledge and skills." She tells me,

The only thing would be—scientific knowledge and skills. I think that's important because everything we do should be based in science and research-based. And that's why we came to school is to learn. But then also it does kind of leave out a little bit, and of course, it's different from person to person. But also using kind of your best judgment, not always based on science but on relationships and communication with people.

Laura similarly comments on how she watched veterinarians at work, and was slowly beginning to realize that there was much more to the profession than the simple application of the science she learned in her lectures,

But doctors have so much experience, so many years of experience. And they see a disease or a situation and they already have a method of, "This works with a lot of my patients. So this is a good method that I've kind of developed." And then, in my head, I'm like, "But that's not what the textbook or this other doctor talked about in their lecture." And so, I really don't know on my own. I need to kind of figure that out for myself too. And I've been trying these last—as it gets closer, trying to kind of step back and be like, "Okay". If it was just me and I don't have a doctor above me to go be like, "Okay. This is what I want to do," to kind of get my mind frame right.

Here, Laura realizes that not only does she need to be making her own decisions as a soon to be veterinarian, but that science can lead in multiple directions, and in reality the practice of veterinary medicine is an embodied one that is always human, and thus variable. While she was taught in the didactic phase of her education that science provides one correct answer, in practice she sees that is not true. Instead, she realizes that multiple solutions are possible, and that the larger context of the patient and the owner determines not only what the most humane approach is, but what the best scientific answer is. Since Kuhn (1962) the acknowledgment that the facts of science are socially constructed within what Latour and Woolgar (1979) term "laboratory life" (in their well-known book by the same name) has been well studied in bench science fields.[1] Laura's observations extend that truth to clinical, field practiced, scientific practice, acknowledging the very human and social construction of what she had previously accepted as inviolate truth from her earlier years in the veterinary education classroom.

Christina also comments on her observations in the teaching hospital that sometimes the veterinarians are fixated on one problem with the body, but they fail to see the larger picture of the patient (animal) in their wholeness,

Because we have the ability to do a lot of things in medicine, especially here in this specialty center where we can do anything.

Maybe it's just that I don't see as much of the benefit because I don't know that much yet. But I just wonder sometimes like, "Why are we continuing to do this stuff when the outcome's not going to be that much different?" . . . So it's kind of about the bigger picture for me, not just like, "Here's this little nodule. We got to fix this." But the dog's dying around this. Then what does that matter?

Faced with the blunt, though false, dichotomy of "science" and "love" the veterinary profession has chosen science, and a notion of professionalism that privileges science and disregards love. Goldberg (2008) frames this debate in medicine as a "tug-of-war between humanism and professionalism" (p. 719). In his work, Goldberg notes examples of this dynamic throughout qualitative research with medical students. Referencing the earlier research of Christakis and Feudtner (1993), Goldberg discusses the frustration of a medical student faced with the dilemma of a woman experiencing homelessness, who is admitted to the hospital for an acute episode of chronic obstructive pulmonary disease. While the woman confides in the medical student that she is currently homeless, she lies to the intern, the student's supervisor, about her situation. The intern is eager to accept the woman's lie and tells the medical student quite bluntly that he wanted her "off his service" (Christakis & Feudtner, 1993, p. 253). Goldberg reflects on this situation much as Christina does in the aforementioned example, writing,

> The student, apparently, sees great irony in narrowly focusing on an acute respiratory problem while ignoring the large threats to health and well-being in this chronically ill patient. Moreover, discharge under these conditions almost guarantees relapse, making the whole effort self-defeating. The intern, however, is uninterested. Whether out of cynicism, resignation, or both, he has learned to define his own professional role just that narrowly. The patient's next admission will belong to someone else.

(p. 719)

The situation that Christina described is different in some respects: because the patient is a dog, not a human, euthanasia is possible, and according to Christina, the dog was actively dying, while the woman discussed in Christakis and Feudtner's (1993) research is not. Yet, the parallels between these two situations are still striking. Christina and the medical student apply a humanist perspective to the suffering they are witnessing, feeling an obligation to animal (Christina) and human (the medical student) welfare. In contrast, their respective superiors are fully immersed in professional worldviews, where the patient (animal or human) must compete for priority with other demands, including ones to science and the process of discovery and to the structural realities of animal and human hospitals. While Christina might have correctly noted that both the prevention of animal suffering and animal welfare are components of the veterinary oath, they are not necessarily the central or driving concern when they confront the demands of professionalism.

Goldberg (2008) discusses research studies that follow the transition of medical students from various states of "outsider" and "insider" to complete insiders, who are fully socialized into the professional world view. For example, Goldberg discusses a student in Parson et al.'s study (2001) who moves from expressing shock at how doctors talked about patients and their families at the beginning of medical school and clinical experiences to understanding how and why that happens, after a month of sleep deprivation and clinical rounds. Heather tells me a similar story, reflecting on her own reaction to a client after sleepless days,

> When I was on ER, we were working 6 days a week and were there 12, 16-hour days. And I mean, near the end, I was just emotionally exhausted to where I was having inappropriate outbursts. I laughed, not to their face, but I laughed at the client, and that's not my personality. I would never laugh at the client, but I was just so exhausted that

I couldn't be myself and regulate my emotions. That's unfortunate because the patient suffers and the client suffers and nobody wins from that.

Goldberg (2008) summarizes the existing research through concluding,

From their [the students'] perspective, their collective, naïve conscience was hitting up against the conventions of professional practice, and, in many cases, it succumbed. As the data suggest, the students evolve over time, willing, for instance, to speak about patients in ways that they themselves used to find disturbing.

(p. 719)

I find echoes of Goldberg's conclusions throughout my research, but most clearly in Chapter 6, where students no longer connect with the animals, who in a veterinary situation are the patients. As they say, they feel "numb" and are often only vaguely aware that there are animals present. Of course, literally they are immersed in animals: they are surrounded by them. But their presence no longer matters to them in any meaningful way. Caught in transitional liminality, students are too exhausted, jaded, and stressed to be able to focus on the animals. Yet, because they are not yet "insiders" or members of the veterinary profession, the norms, rhythms, friendships, politics, and long relationships (good and bad) that their supervisors are enmeshed in are invisible to them. The overwhelming majority of students in my study could not talk to their supervisors about their feelings or experiences: only a couple of students mentioned a few fleeting conversations. Love slowly disappears, to be replaced by a distant professionalism that students accept as the norm. Like the medical students that Goldberg discusses, the participants in my study begin to understand that there is a "trade" underway: they must leave their humanistic impulses behind to be able to finally wear the white coat and become a veterinarian.

In Chapter 6, I discussed some of the ways that students found small spaces of resistance and renewal during their final year of clinical rotations: through insisting that clients be called "mom" and "dad" in the small animal hospital, to finding ways to honor animals' lives at the moment of death. As they do this, they re-establish the centrality of animals to veterinary practice, but they also center themselves and their clients as human beings.

As I move into the rest of this chapter, I focus on various pathways forward for telling new stories of animals and humans, drawing on my participants' stories and literature outside of veterinary medicine.

A WORLD BEYOND: OPENING TO ANIMAL CONNECTIONS

Throughout my years of interviews with students, the amount of energy and focus they had available to maintain and strengthen their connections with animals varied. Early on, they realized that animals, in their whole beings, were not a priority for their veterinary education. Thus these relationships were nurtured in private spaces of their life, both through their own animals or those of their friends, and in a few precious moments during their veterinary life where they could take a respite from their obligations to the profession and remember and revisit themselves. Kiara tells me about a calf who came into the large animal hospital while she was doing one of her clinical rotations in large animal surgery,

> a few weeks ago, I was on large animal surgery for a second time. And I had this calf this came into that had contracted tendons, very just stiff kind of walking on its toes. And I had it for about two weeks out of the three weeks.
>
> And it was just really nice to be able to see her progress and everything and run around.
>
> We named her Jorsie, [she] didn't have a name but we were just like, "Oh, it's Jorsie" because she was just so funny, always had her tongue out and her eyes were buggy. And the owner came in to pick her up and were all just surrounding Jorsie, taking pictures, and then we made this little birthday hat for her and took a picture of her.

Kiara and her classmates were aware that Jorsie was a commodity to her owner and a very expensive investment, telling me, "I think that a sibling of hers was sold for $40,000 and so she was good stock and so if anything (he) wanted to just kind of get some use out of her because of her good genetics."

Despite the fact that Jorsie had no name when she entered the veterinary hospital, and that she was primarily valued (Jones, 2003) in economic terms, Kiara told me that the owner was genuinely moved emotionally through seeing the relationship between the veterinary team and Jorsie. Kiara continues and discusses the client's reaction to the impromptu party for Jorsie,

> **Nadine:** What did the owner think about it?
> **Kiara:** He was actually really pleased.
> **Nadine:** Really?
> **Kiara:** Yeah. He took the hat with him. He was like, "Oh, what the heck." He was like, "Wow, I didn't realize that you all really liked her like that so."

While Kiara's story suggests that veterinary professional's approach to an animal can help to shape and change a client's relationship with their animal (pet or not), the dynamic can also work in the opposite direction. For example, I talked with many of the students about the status of pigs in the large animal hospital. Much like the horses that Vermilya (2012) discusses in her study, by the time of my research, pigs were becoming a "border" animal in many instances. Formally admitted to the large animal hospital, some pigs were clearly pets and there were quiet conversations about whether these pet pigs belonged in the commodity-oriented large animal hospital. Michelle tells me about one of these pigs who had come into the large animal hospital as a patient and how the owner's relationship with the pig had influenced how the veterinary students treated her,

> So because when her owner dropped her off, she said, "Don't treat her like a market pig." And so her student was like, "I'm going to paint her nails. They don't paint market pig's nails." So I mean, she's a really good pig. She laid around and slept all day like she was living the life, for sure.

At that point, Michelle pulled out her phone to show me the pig's nails, saying, "Just wait. Look at what Amy did, painted her little piggies."

My participants' connections with animals and the human–animal bond were exceedingly important to students. Many assumed that it was in the veterinary oath and were shocked when I told them that it was not. Others read through the oath and then proceeded to discuss it as if the human–animal bond was a core component of their professional vows, though of course, it is not.

These moments that students describe to me are fleeting. But they are strong in their memories as significant life experiences (Chalwa, 1998), shaping the core of the type of veterinary medicine that they perhaps hope to practice, one day. Yet, they are also aware that their connections are not openly valued or discussed, and they tend to bury or discount them as side anecdotes, not ones that are core to the profession. Instead, the students position these experiences, in many ways, as ones that remind them of their humanism, *instead of* their professionalism (Goldberg, 2008).

COGNITIVE ETHOLOGY: SCIENCE AND NEW ANIMAL STORIES

While fields such as veterinary medicine (and my own, of education) continue to valorize Cartesian dualism and Eurocentric science/scientism, perhaps somewhat ironically, science itself is now undermining that split, demonstrating through multiple fields including neuroscience, that Cartesian dualism is, as a scientific proposition, simply false. As neurologist Damasio (1994) writes in his (aptly titled) book, *Descartes' Error,*

> Reason may not be as pure as most of us think it is or wish it were, that emotions and feelings may not be intruders in the bastion of reason at all: they may enmeshed in its networks.

> **(p. xii)**

Rollin (2019) specifically discusses Descartes' arguments against the need for moral concern for animals, as they were simply "machines." Rollin expresses his dismay at how this (mistaken) philosophical position continues to influence veterinary medicine, writing, "As I began to work more and more on animal ethics and animal consciousness, I was astounded by the number of people who continued the Cartesian tradition of denying thought and feeling to animals" (2019, p. 393).

These shifts suggest that there is a way to reconnect love to the veterinary profession. As Lawrence argues, "We mut accept the fact that love for animals can augment veterinary science rather than hinder it, and that love should no longer be devalued in the profession" (p. 972). Writing from the field of primatology, Frans de Waal underscores this reality for scientists doing research with animals, arguing for the (unavoidable) centrality of feelings, emotions, and attachment, "I would turn the stereotype of the unfeeling scientist around and say that it is the rare investigator who is not at some level attached to the furry, feathered, or slippery creatures he or she works with" (2001, p. 39).

One of the emergent fields that is relevant to finding and valuing love in the veterinary profession is cognitive ethology. Cognitive ethologists use observation and interaction to tell the stories of animals' lives. They often spend hundreds (if not thousands) of hours observing how animals interact, trying to discern patterns of behavior. However, in opposition to behaviorism and positivist science, cognitive ethologists examine this behavior not as instinct but as meaningful actions that represent how animals perceive the world, feel, and act (Bekoff & Jamieson, 1990). As Bekoff and Jamieson (1990) argue, "Good ethologists try to study animals without the ideological blinders of positivism and behaviorism, two views which have the effect of reinforcing belief in human uniqueness" (p. 157). In contrast, they look for evolutionary continuity in the stories they tell, assuming, following Darwin, that differences among species are differences in degree not kind (Bekoff, 2000). These are not ideas that are unknown to veterinary medicine, as Rollin (2019) explores in his discussion of Darwin and early studies of what he terms "animal mentation" and its demise in a world influenced by Descartes and behaviorism.

As a field, cognitive ethology is comparatively new, with its formal recognition credited to Donald Griffin's (1976) book on animal awareness. In the past two decades, the influence and reach of the field has expanded considerably, because as Bekoff (2006) suggests, cognitive ethology is

> the unifying science for understanding the subjective, emotional, empathic, and moral lives of animals, because it is essential to know what animals do, think, and feel as they go about their daily routines in the company of their friends and when they are alone.

(p. 71)

Bekoff, a prominent cognitive ethologist, is well known for his research on play behavior among dogs, coyotes, and wolves, and studies of morality in animals, particularly questions about fairness, reciprocity, relationships, altruism, and empathy (Bekoff & Pierce, 2010).

Cognitive ethology intersects with fields such as philosophy, psychology, anthropology, religion, evolutionary biology, primatology, and neuroscience. Griffin's research was originally criticized "as anecdotal and anthropomorphic, as bad science, and as just plain muddled thinking" (Allen & Bekoff, 1997, p. 4). However, more recently, many of its findings on animal cognition and emotion have been replicated by lab-based researchers in numerous canine cognition labs (at, for example, Barnard, Yale, Duke, and the University of Florida) and primate cognition labs (for example, at Columbia, Emory, and most famously the Max Planck Institute for Evolutionary Anthropology in Germany). There has been growing consensus among researchers working within multiple scientific traditions about the existence and importance of animal sentience, cognition, and emotion with the adoption of the Cambridge Declaration on Consciousness in 2012 (Jones, 2013).

The stories that cognitive ethologists tell range across species (from bees to elephants) and include a broad range of emotions and cognitive abilities. While cognitive ethology acknowledges that positivist science does not traditionally value stories, Bekoff (2007) argues that the "plural of anecdote is data" (p. 121). In an interview on *Nature* entitled, "Animal Odd Couples: Studying the Emotional Lives of Animals" Bekoff recalls that after he wrote about observing a magpie funeral, his inbox was flooded with emails from people who had witnessed similar magpie behavior (Public Broadcasting System, 2012). Given the consistency of these stories, he is inclined to give credence them credit as data, arguing that cumulatively they tell us something about how magpies mourn. At the same time, ethologists recognize that generalizations about species-linked behavior has limits, and that it is always necessary to primarily consider the experience of the individual animal, which—like in humans—may differ dramatically from that of the species in general. Ethologists look for patterns that are meaningful and can tell us something that is important for us to know about a species, at the same time understanding that each sentient being has his or her own experience and capacity for meaning-making.

Cognitive ethology is also self-reflexive about its own practice as Bekoff and Jamieson (1990) write, "Cognitive ethology, like other human enterprises, is value-laden" (p. 157). For example, cognitive ethologists are concerned about how human values and priorities shape how humans approach studying animals. They write, "The fixation of ethologists, psychologists, and anthropologists on such topics as aggression and dominance, for example, tells us more about them than about the animals they study" (p. 157). This is a singularly critical point that is crucial for understanding all human endeavors, including how we think about and approach the study of animals. As Scott, an influential historian of the construction of knowledge says in 2014 interview reflecting on her canonical (1991) essay on experience,

> It's Foucault who best formulated this genealogical approach, arguing that "events" were not things that happened, but conceptual changes that altered the mindset of a culture or a society or group. If you believe that how we think about things is how we know them, then it is our categories of thought that create knowledge. It then becomes very important to know where those categories come from, how they have been used and by whom, what they permit us to think and what they rule out of consideration.

(Hesford & Diedrich, 2014, p. 200)

As Bekoff suggests, the obsession with certain ways of studying and engaging animals is reflective not of the animals and their true essence or being but of the categories that humans have used to make sense of animals. Whose interests are served by studying animal aggression and dominance? What happen, instead, when scientists begin to instead study, for example, animal empathy, as primatologist de Waal (2009) has done for many decades now?

One of the most central theoretical frames of knowledge that needs to be questioned and rethought within veterinary medicine and associated fields is anthropomorphism. While anthropomorphism is often dismissed without thought as bad science, the very roots of the idea as a category of knowledge need to be more thoroughly interrogated, following Foucault (1972) and Scott (1991). Openings to new science and thus new stories, require rethinking accepted (capital T) "Truths" and replacing them with other ways of understanding humans in relationship to the natural world.

For natural scientists, for example Bekoff, anthropomorphism is understood as a part of the human condition. Bekoff (2007) writes, "When we anthropomorphize, we're doing what comes naturally, and we shouldn't be punished for it. It's part of who we are" (p. 125). However, as both Bekoff (2007) and de Waal argue, it is important that as humans studying non-human behavior, we practice what Bekoff terms "careful" (2007, p. 126) anthropomorphism and De Waal (2001) terms "animalcentric" anthropomorphism, which he distinguishes from "anthropocentric anthropomorphism." In other words, they insist that we acknowledge our human values and beliefs. While we can never bracket them, we nonetheless understand that our priorities are not the priorities of all species: it is part of being humble as a researcher (and a person) and accepting that not all species (or humans) see or experience the world in the same way. De Waal (2001) makes an apt and relevant analogy to human behavior,

> Animalcentric anthropomorphism must be sharply distinguished from anthropocentric anthropomorphism. . . . The first takes the animal's perspective, the second takes ours. It is a bit like people we all know, who buy us presents that *we* like versus people who buy us presents that *they* like. The later have not yet reached a mature form of empathy, and perhaps never will (italics in original).

(p. 77)

For cognitive ethologists, the researcher him, her, or their self is always part of the story. We are also, however, always aware that our perspectives on others' experiences—whether human or non-human animals—is only partial. We see as much of another's "truth" as we can and combine our stories (our research) with others' stories to bring about change.

HUMAN STORIES AND ANIMAL INTERSECTIONS: VETERINARY HUMANITIES

Cognitive ethologists focus on telling animal stories, which is a critical corrective to patterns of thinking and creating knowledge that deny that animals have stories. In addition, veterinary medicine can also benefit from exploring and learning from fields that center human experiences and stories, and of course, from the interactions, connections, and disconnections between humans and animals. Veterinary humanities is a new field, one that brings together scholars and researchers from the humanities, social sciences, and inside veterinary medicine to begin to rethink some of the fundamental precepts of the profession. In their call for members, Skipper and Gray (2021) address the very human problems that veterinary practitioners confront every day, and the limits of the profession's ability to address these problems given its current approach,

> Yet veterinary knowledge is still generally conceptualised in terms of evidence-based medicine and quantitative research, which are vital tools for improving clinical interventions but less applicable to issues of human behaviour.
> To tackle these complex and difficult human problems we need to think differently and step away from the current veterinary world view.

(p. 233)

Skipper and Gray (2021) continue to discuss how the development of veterinary humanities would benefit from exploring medical humanities, a well-established field,

Medical humanities has been a recognised discipline for 50 years and is embedded in medical training. It equips doctors to communicate more effectively, responding flexibly to their patients' needs, and helps to build resilience by fostering a reflective outlook. However, while there has recently been some valuable humanities work in the veterinary sector, veterinary humanities has not yet been independently recognised in the same way.

(p. 233)

One of the most important subfields in the medical humanities is narrative medicine, as developed by Charon (2006) as a way for doctors to both listen to and hear their patients and to begin to see them as more than a clinical diagnosis, but as full, complex human beings. Charon writes,

To know what patients endure at the hands of illness and therefore to be of clinical help requires that doctors enter the world of patients, if only imaginatively, and to see and interpret these worlds from the patients' point of view.

(p. 9)

Charon's (2006) work is best known for the concept of the "Parallel Chart." She writes how she explains to medical students how to use a Parallel Chart,

Every day, you write in the hospital chart about each of your patients. You know exactly what to write there, and the form in which to write it. You write about your patient's current complaints, the results of the physical exam, laboratory findings, opinions of consultants, and the plan. If your patient dying of prostate cancer reminds you of your grandfather, who died of that disease last summer, and each time you go into the patient's room, you weep for your grandfather, you cannot write that in the hospital chart, we will not let you. And yet it has to be written somewhere. You write it in the Parallel Chart.

(pp. 155–156)

Charon is careful to distinguish between a diary, for example, and the Parallel Chart. The Parallel Chart is not self-indulgent (as a journal or diary might be) and it is not, primarily, for the clinician. Instead, as she explains, the Parallel Chart is "narrative writing in the service of the care of a particular patient" (p. 157).

Adams (2011) extends this insight further, into an understanding of how the Parallel Chart, or a similar mechanism, can be used to grapple with how that patient is socially situated and the very real everyday struggles that bring both complexity and challenges to everyday life,

not only hearing a patient's complaints about the symptoms of multiple sclerosis, but also considering how she is affected by an environment of broken bus lifts and elevators, and by struggles with her insurance company and an unaccommodating workplace.

(p. B20)

More recently, Sufian et al. (2020) have developed what they term the "Health Humanities Portrait Approach" which centers people's lives through their social context, instead of their diagnosis. They explain,

> Like a key characteristic of a portrait in art, the Portrait Approach *centers the patient* while also revealing the larger structures shaping that voice. . . . By focusing on the patient, educators and learners are more likely to think of this person as more than his/her/their disease.

(Sufian et al., 2020, p. 464, emphasis is the author's)

While slightly different than the Health Humanities Portrait Approach, portraiture, as developed by Lawrence-Lightfoot (Lawrence-Lightfoot & Davis, 1997) has been used in my own field of education for many decades. While not without critique, portraiture is currently experiencing a revival as a method that centers stories and forges human connection (Bruhn & Jimenez, 2020; Lawrence-Lightfoot, 2005. For critique, see English, 2000).

From the related field of qualitative inquiry Pelias (2015) suggests that "We should continue to fund our work with philosophical and theoretical thought, but we should not let philosophy and theory trump the power of a teller offering a narrative that demands cognitive and affective engagement" (p. 609). Pelias returns us to stories, arguing that they are at the core of what is valuable, unique, and indispensable about qualitative inquiry: the ability to foreground the human story (ies) not solely for the mere proliferation of stories, but for a purpose: for social change and to tell "stories that matter" (p. 611).

The centrality of human experience, whether explored through portraiture, stories, or other forms of discovery and illumination return me to Goldberg's insistence that humanism—in all of its complexity—needs to be at the core of the health professions. In the specific case of medical education, he concludes that there is a pressing need to emphasize humanism over professionalism,

> Let them [medical students] learn to subordinate their medical, professional identity to their essential human character, for our goal is physicians who see their medicine as part of a commitment to humanism, not physicians who superficially incorporate values of humanism into their picture of medicine.

(2008, p. 721)

Instead of invalidating concerns about a patient in the service of professionalism, as was evidenced in the story I told about Christina's animal patient and Goldberg's parallel example of a human patient, medical humanities insists that these portraits and stories are at the center of medical practice. In this framework, the stories that students tell me are not simply distractions from the "real" work of veterinary medicine, they *are* the work. I imagine how much less trauma would have come out, in gushes, in my final interviews with students if they had had meaningful opportunities to engage with their own narratives, and those of their patients and clients, during their veterinary education, as a constitutive element of the curriculum.

The field of medicine, and related fields such as narrative medicine and medical humanities, focus exclusively on humans in their multiple roles as patients, doctors, nurses, staff, and families. Of course, many of these human families include animals, and there are emergent attempts to begin conversations between fields such as medical humanities and animal studies (Kirk et al., 2019). The social work field has a well-developed literature on the role of pets in human lives, including but not limited to the relatively new field of veterinary social work (Arkow, 2020; Holcombe et al., 2016; Rauktis & Hoy-Gerlach, 2020; Risley-Curtiss et al., 2013). The COVID-19 pandemic and the increased focus on the role of animals (especially pets) in people's lives is accelerating the pace of research in this area. Certainly, a human hospital patient's mental and physical well-being is impacted by the worry and concern that the person has for a beloved pet from whom they are now separated.

In the veterinary field, animals are the patients: the humans surround the patient, with the animal remaining at the center. Yet, as Skipper and Gray (2021) emphasize, veterinary medicine is enmeshed in often intractable human problems. Thus, veterinary medicine is positioned at the nexus of multiple fields that allows it to tell three types of stories: stories of animals, stories of their human guardians or caregivers (including veterinary doctors and staff), and stories of the connections and disconnections between humans and animals.

This focus on stories allows us to see each animal patient as an individual. It is evident through my research, and that of others' research in the related field of the human–animal bond, that of course that happens all the time in veterinary medicine, as it happens in our own lives (e.g., Ware, 2018). I personally do not experience my dog as "dog," but as "Eddie" who happens to be a dog. I honor and respect the fact that he is a different species than I am, and thus has different needs, desires, capacities, and limits. I do not attempt to try to make him a human or do human things. I recognize his essential "dogginess." Yet, at the same time, he is clearly an individual: he is not generic "dog." As Montgomery (2018) tells us, "Knowing someone who belongs to another species can enlarge your soul in surprising ways" (p. II). Note that Montgomery uses the word "someone" to refer to the beings we share the planet with who happen to belong to a different species. Contrast the word "someone" with "thing"—a word that as I noted in previous chapters, became an increasingly common way for the students to refer to animals as they became socialized into the veterinary field.

There are also rich possibilities in expanding the insights of narrative medicine and the medical humanities to veterinary practice, for both humans and animals. In the veterinary field, such innovations as Charon's (2006) "Parallel Chart" and Sufian et al.'s (2020) "Health Humanities Portrait" can be used for animal patients, for human clients, and for understanding and honoring the interaction between them. My students' impulses to connect, to care, and to explore multiple forms of love for their animal patients can be strengthened, while at the same time they can find ways to navigate the multiple tensions in their human interactions.

Of course, these new approaches open difficult and often buried conversations in veterinary medicine about the role of animals in our human society. What does it mean, as Skipper and Gray (2021) suggest, to "step away from the current veterinary world view" (p. 233)? While Skipper and Gray are concerned primarily with humans, my questions suggest a wider lens and scope. How can engagement with conversations and changes outside of veterinary medicine lead to a more humane field, both for animals and humans? Is it inevitable that veterinary medicine remains entangled in practices that cause animals to suffer and die? What other possibilities exist in the paradigm of "new love?"

NOTE

1 Latour is often considered the founder of the field of STS (Science and Technology Studies) and his legacy in the sociology and philosophy of science is complex, and beyond the scope of this book to discuss in full. While his scholarship has garnered serious and heavy critique, its validity and import are also undeniable. See Latour (2018) and Kofman (2018) for an in-depth interview with Latour about the "post-truth" world in the age of Trump.

8 Turning Stories into New Love
Possibilities

Oxygen. Our common bond. Our common need. Our common wish. To breathe and to breathe freely.

McArthur (2017, p. 11)

there is nowhere to hide, nowhere to go, no great beyond outside of this world. We are forever bound, and our task is to re-create those bonds so that they are humane and just.

Dolby (2003, p. 60)

A troubled love is at the heart of the veterinary education. The students in my study entered veterinary education torn between their connections and disconnections from animals. Throughout their four-year journey, they wrestled with these contradictions largely alone. Most came to simply accept that there was no other way forward: that they needed to ignore their feelings and discomfort and to focus on the task that was before them.

Some academics from inside veterinary education are beginning to understand that students' feelings and emotions are important and must be addressed somehow through the veterinary curriculum. For the most part, the proposed pedagogies focus only on humans: animals as sentient beings are largely ignored. Historically, veterinary medicine has been governed by this approach: one that tacitly and quietly accepts that animal suffering and human violence toward animals is necessary for the everyday functioning of the profession. However, more recently, societal pressure on these norms and practices has required the profession to rethink its response to how it both represents and participates in these acts of violence for example, through the slaughter of animals for food (Croney, 2010; Croney, 2014; Croney & Reynnells, 2008).[1] I start this chapter with a recent (2019) example from the veterinary education literature that represents an approach that—while on the surface innovative—in actuality only reinscribes the human/animal binary, and further buries the structural contradictions and tensions in veterinary education. I then move to discussing openings and possibilities, returning to stories that can help all of us who care for and about animals, humans, and the planet, to re-imagine new forms and ways to love.

DOI: 10.1201/9781003269984-8

AN OLD STORY

As I discussed in Chapter 4, encounters with dead animals, witnessing, and participating in the process of killing, is extremely challenging and upsetting for (some, not
all) students. Emotions are always a part of veterinary practice, particularly when
animals are killed whether through euthanasia or slaughter (Hulsbergen et al., 2019;
Littlewood et al., 2020). While euthanasia is (ideally, though not always) performed
to relive animal suffering, slaughter is more complicated, because the animal is dying
not to relieve his or her own pain, but for human consumption. Recognizing the challenges of normalizing this experience for students in a world that is increasingly
conscious of both animal welfare and animal rights, Hulsbergen et al. (2019) write
about their research on teaching humane slaughter, set in the context of veterinary
education in The Netherlands (p 128).[2] As they discuss, learning these techniques is
required for veterinary school graduation in the Netherlands,

> To cater for these authorizations, students of veterinary medicine participate in a pro-
> gram of theoretical and practical training on stunning and bleeding of cattle in their
> final year of the Master's program. . . . Anecdotal and experiential evidence suggests
> that this program has a profound effect on the students' well-being, with students
> sometimes showing a strong emotional response (e.g., crying) and very occasionally
> refusing to take part in the activity, which means they cannot graduate. It is clear that
> emotions are relevant to the process of learning to slaughter cattle.
>
> **(p. 128)**

Working in the old story, Hulsbergen et al. (2019) only recognize and acknowledge
human emotions, and how these emotions might impede students' progress toward
their veterinary degree. They concede that this course may be particularly difficult
for students,

> A course on humane slaughter is clearly a demanding situation for veterinary stu-
> dents, in which positive emotions related to learning a new skill are at risk of being
> outweighed by negative emotions related to killing a living creature. Most aspects of
> the veterinarian's job are aimed at improving the health of animals; learning about
> *humane slaughter*, therefore, involves crossing an emotional threshold.
>
> **(p. 128, emphasis is the author's)**

Hulsbergen et al. (2019) then go on to describe their research study in which they
attempted to help students confront their emotions while first witnessing a video of
bovine slaughter, then spending time thinking about and picturing themselves performing the slaughter, and finally noting their emotional response through selecting
from 40 cards that depicted different emotions. The intervention reported limited
results, having no statistical impact on students' emotional response. Perhaps this is
not surprising, as the inherent contradiction in being asked to love and kill simultaneously is not openly discussed but instead is managed through (what may appear
to students to be) a game. The reality of the killing of the cow is not changed, and
is, in many ways, trivialized through reducing it to an exercise in selecting your

emotion from a set of cards. Pedersen (2013), writing from the perspective of critical animal studies, also discusses her ethnographic fieldwork with veterinary students in Sweden who similarly experience a pig slaughterhouse for the first time. Pedersen concludes that their emotional response is considered by the veterinary faculty and other supervisors to be an "*an integral and necessary part of*" veterinary education (2013, p. 717, emphasis is the author's).

Glaringly absent from Hulsbergen et al.'s research (2019) is any recognition that the animals themselves have feelings and emotions, a reality that *is* engaged by Pedersen. Cows, pigs, and other animals are not inanimate objects: they are sentient beings who feel, who think, and who suffer (Bekoff, 2000, 2007, 2013; Bekoff & Pierce, 2010; King, 2013, 2017). We, as humans, are always already entangled with cows and every other species on the planet (Gruen, 2015). Hulsbergen et al. (2019) avoid this reality and thus refuse to engage with the core issues of conflicting emotions and priorities in veterinary medicine. What does it mean to kill your patient, not to end the patient's suffering, but so that a person can have a steak dinner?

SIGNS OF CHANGE

In most corners of veterinary medicine, the silence about the contradictions in its practice remains muted and hidden perhaps discussed privately, but not publicly. There are times, however, when very public collisions may force reflection and reconsideration. One such recent story revolves around Esther the Wonder Pig, and her family's ongoing relationship with the University of Guelph in Canada.

In 2012, Steve Jenkins and Derek Walters adopted Esther from a person who told them that she was a "mini" or "teacup" pig. Instead, it quickly became apparent to Jenkins and Walters that Esther was the size of a commercial pig, raised to be slaughtered for food. She rapidly surpassed 650 lbs. Despite the challenges of sharing your home with an enormous pig, Jenkins and Walters realized that the emotional attachment they felt for Esther was no different than their attachment to their dogs. In their book about their experience living with Esther, they relate the moment when they came to clear consciousness about the emotional contradictions in understanding this reality (Jenkins & Walter, 2016). One night, a few weeks after adopting Esther, they were cooking dinner, which happened to include bacon. They looked at what was in their pan on the stovetop and then at Esther, sitting patiently next to them as they cooked. The understanding that it could be Esther in their pan was immediate and painful: they tossed the bacon in the trash. Within a few years, they had sold their suburban Toronto home (where Esther was legally not allowed to live), purchased a rural farm in Ontario, and started the "Happily Ever Esther Farm Sanctuary." Esther lives her life with her parents Steve (Jenkins) and Derek (Walter), and along with her friends Corno (a turkey) and Phil (a dog) is an ambassador for kindness and compassion for farm animals.

By 2017, Esther had outlived her life expectancy as a commercial pig destined for slaughter at a young age and was starting to develop health problems. Admitted to the Ontario Veterinary College (OVC), she needed a CT scan. But a scanner that could accommodate Esther was not available at the OVC or at any veterinary facility in

Canada. The closest one was a few hundred miles away in the United States, but that involved a potentially dangerous journey for her, and because she was legally classified as "livestock" a three-week isolation quarantine period before she could re-enter Canada. With limited options and with a family member in dire need, Jenkins and Walters went on a fundraising blitz, appealing to their millions of supporters to raise over $650,000 CAD to purchase the Pegaso scanner to donate to the OVC, and to pay for its delivery and necessary renovations at the OVC to accommodate the scanner. Esther had the first scan in 2018, and now the OVC has a scanner that can be used to diagnose and eventually treat large animals throughout Canada. For example, the scanner allows a horse to be scanned in a standing position, eliminating the need for risky anesthesia to scan the horse lying down.

As a celebrity patient, Esther of course received compassionate care at the veterinary college hospital. Yet, the OVC is no different philosophically from the College of Veterinary Medicine at CMU, where I conducted this research study. By 2019, Esther, who had continued health problems, was again an in-patient at OVC, with her parents setting up a mock living room in her stall in the large animal hospital and broadcasting regular updates on Esther to her fans through Facebook live. Yet, on the same campus, the Ontario Agricultural College was happily publicizing its upcoming pig roast, with a vivid graphic on its poster of a cartoon pig roasting over an open fire. Esther's fan base was outraged, and after on-line petitions and media coverage, the image on the poster was changed, though the event itself (rebranded a "barbecue") was not cancelled (Axworthy, 2019; Khan, 2019). Esther's parents volunteered to donate Beyond™ (vegan) sausages and burgers for the event. The OVC, of course, was quiet. The contradictions and entangled emotions were, no doubt, apparent to many: they could treat Esther, pet her, chat with her parents, and then stroll across campus to eat one of her same species for lunch, at a well-publicized and university-sanctioned event.

As a global society, we are beginning to rethink how we categorize animals, and our relationship with them. This movement is evident not only in the astounding (and unexpected) success of Esther the Wonder Pig, but in the overwhelming and rapid public opposition to the pig roast on OVC's campus: an event that would have gone unnoticed in years past. Beyond academia, there are vital and important movements worldwide to rethink how we as humans use animals for food, for entertainment, and for research (Bekoff & Pierce, 2017; Dolby, 2018; Foer, 2009; Gluck, 2016; Reese, 2018).

These are real changes, but they also help us to confront uncomfortable truths about how our increasing emotional relationships with some animals (companion animals or pets) lead to the intensification of suffering for other animals who are slaughtered for food. These are also challenging issues for veterinary colleges, as pet food companies and pet pharmaceutical companies are often embedded in veterinary education. For example, many of the students in my study applied to be the veterinary school representative for a pet food company, and one of them, Heather, was hired. She told me,

> There's a program through the school where students get half off for food, and staff gets 25% off. And every week the food gets shipped in, and we just put stickers on it

and open the store. When I first got hired [the training] took place in [name of state redacted]. And it was great, because I got to network with some of the [name of pet food company] people, learn about the corporate side of vet med, got to see some of the research animals there. . . . We got to see where they do the research, and I was really impressed. So they have two areas where they have their cats and their dogs, and they seem like they live better than a lot of dogs do that live in homes. Like they're well-socialized, they're in dog groups all day, they're in large kennels. And when they do research on them, it's like they put two bowls out, and they see which one they prefer to eat out of. It was nice, it gave me a good perspective on animal research, at least that one specific example, because obviously not all of them are going to be like that. But it showed me animal research can be done correctly. They had really great welfare standards. Like those dogs are really well taken care of and they seem really happy. And the cats were just in big rooms where they had stuff on the walls where they could climb up.

Last year I got $10 an hour. This year I get $13.50. It's just kind of organizing the store and responding to people's emails and stuff. But it's fun, I like it.

Another student in my study, Marissa, was hired as a veterinary student representative for a pet pharmaceutical corporation. She tells me she was paid $500 per semester. She explains her responsibilities to me,

I loved it. It is the biggest veterinary pharmaceutical company in the world, so that comes with a powerful punch. It was cool. I get to pick a topic each semester. So my first ever topic, we collaborated with another club and [talked about] a portal, like a Facebook for veterinary professionals, but it's not so social media-esq. In the spring, I did a lecture, it's a drug called Cerenia, and it . . . the thing is, we have a lot of products, but it's not my job to pitch products, *it's my job to show a topic in veterinary medicine, and then, oh, by the way, this drug does that*. It was like the vomiting cat case that the first and second years loved, because it helped them to study for an exam that week. And then our anti-vomiting drug, which is really successful. That was really cool, I had a full house.

(my emphasis)

Neither Heather nor Marissa is reflective about how these two major pet corporations may be using them for peer-to-peer influence and marketing. Pet food companies' contracts with veterinary schools create marketing opportunities: vet students who begin to use this pet food (usually available at a discount) for their own pets will go on to recommend the brand to their clients and sell it through their veterinary practice. Veterinary students never have the opportunity to discuss and reflect on the pain and suffering that is caused through the slaughter of animals to feed our pets, and the damage done to the environment through these practices (Ward et al., 2020). While "clean" pet food is still in its infancy, the development of more sustainable, healthier ways to feed our pets (and ourselves) is critical. These are the real ethical dilemmas at the core of veterinary education. And while I can attest that Cerenia can be a miracle drug for some animals (from my own experience with my pets—I have some in my kitchen cabinet), I have also witnessed it have absolutely no effects. A true veterinary education would provide students with the opportunity to examine the (non-company sponsored) research on Cerenia, the pharmacology, and its success and failure in actual patients. It would also include frank discussions about how laboratory animals—all sentient beings—suffer so that new drugs are developed to treat diseases in both humans and companion animals (Gluck, 2016). Given the enormous cost to other animals and the environment, is it ethical to even keep pets (Pierce, 2016)?

OPENING TO NEW LOVE

In 2021, Jane Goodall (2021) was joined by more than 80 other world leaders in the fields of animal welfare, animal rights, and conservation in a joint open letter to the Associated Press, calling for a change in animal pronouns. As they assert,

> Mass media, which defaults to this guide in particular, has a great influence on our perception and therefore has an enormous responsibility to portray nonhuman animals as precisely as possible. This is especially true considering the overlap of nonhuman animals and social justice issues that are being increasing covered by journalists.
>
> Yet the current references to them as *it, that* and *which* reduces individual nonhuman animals deserving of our understanding, respect, and protection to mere objects to be owned and exploited for utilitarian purposes.

(n.p., italics are the author's)

They conclude,

> For language to achieve accurate communication of the world around us that allows us to educate ourselves, make informed decisions, and navigate a way forward, it must continuously evolve. The change would be a simple, yet monumental, step towards promoting accuracy in communication and ending the objectification of nonhuman animals we live amongst.

(n.p.)

Language, of course, has vital implications for the veterinary profession. What does it mean to categorize animals as "small" and "large"? What message does it send when a veterinary school has a "food" animal track (Croney, 2014; Vermilya, 2015)? Are clients at a veterinary hospital owners, guardians, or parents? Veterinary students in my study became accustomed to language that repeatedly referred animals as "things" and "stuff" reflecting the objectification that concerns Goddall and the other signatories.

The letter reflects theoretical shifts that move closer to understanding that humans are animals, and thus the limits of relying on models for change that bury and disregard that truth (Challenger, 2021). For example, Goldberg's insistence on centering humanism in opposition to professionalism is useful, in certain circumstances, but it is also limiting in that it emphasizes and re-marks the species divide, underscoring that what is important is our "humanness" in (silent) contrast to our "animalness." In this way, students in my study are both learning with and about animals, and yet are themselves "learning animals"—all animals, including humans, can and do learn. Instead of following Descartes and privileging the false dichotomy of body and mind, what would it mean to follow Darwin, and instead revel in the continuities between humans and other animals?

To do this would mean to both understand and honor that it is a (uniquely human) problem to assume "that animals can't speak for themselves" (Donald, 2019). In my early interviews with students for this book, many of them told me that they wanted to become veterinarians because animals can't speak and thus humans must take on that role for an animal. Jennifer's comment is representative,

> because it's an animal, it can't speak, we have to be their voice, especially being in our profession we have to be able to try to understand what they are trying to tell us, see what is best for them.

But, of course, animals can and do speak, all the time. The assumption that they do not is a fundamental human error, that in the era of the anthropocene, we can no longer afford to believe, if we hope to save the planet for future generations. As Beston (1928) reflected almost a century ago, "They are not brethren, they are not underlings: they are other nations, caught with ourselves in the net of life and time, fellow prisoners of the splendor and travail of the earth" (p. 25). Beston suggests that our first steps toward change must be to accept animals as equal inhabitants on the planet. That means reconsidering fundamental questions about what is acceptable human use of animals, considering the urgent needs of the planet.

The results of this entanglement are becoming increasingly evident. Two significant recent contexts, the acceleration of climate change and the COVID-19 pandemic, have centered this truth. For example, the significant destruction in the Brazilian Amazon from fires in 2019 was a direct result of land clearing for cattle production. Even before the fires, the continual clearing of the land to graze cattle threatened the biodiversity of that region, with ripple effects throughout the globe. Later that year, a wet market in Wuhan, China, was reportedly the source of the COVID-19 global pandemic, as the virus jumped from a wild animal to a human. The summer of 2021, as I finish this book, has been a season of extremes of fire, water, temperatures, and the continued ravages of COVID-19. While many veterinarians are concerned about climate change, they also report that they received little to no education about these critical topics during their veterinary education (Kramer et al., 2020). The natural world is telling us humans, quite clearly, that the current reality is not sustainable.

FINDING OXYGEN AND BREATH

McArthur's reflection on oxygen, the opening epigraph of this chapter, is particularly poignant and telling in 2021, as I finish writing this book. In the midst of the devastation of the worldwide COVID-19 pandemic, hundreds of thousands of people in India and then throughout the world died because they simply could not breathe, and there was no oxygen. We, all of us animals on this shared planet, rely on oxygen for survival.

In her book, McArthur relates how she found a small shard of plexiglass, inscribed with the word "oxygen" as she searched the ruins of a former animal testing site in New Mexico. As she stood silently, remembering all the animal lives that had been lost there, and the humans who had been forever scarred, she took this one word, "oxygen" as a sign that was is important is to breath and to hold fast and tight, for change is coming.

Almost 20 years ago, in 2003, I wrote about the bonds that surround us as human beings on a shared planet: an excerpt from that article is the second epigraph to this chapter. At the time, I was focused on the ongoing (and always, it seems elusive) quest for all humans to have access to what they need to live with dignity, to be able to both survive and to thrive. Clean water, adequate food and shelter, medical care, education, and hope. Sadly, many on the planet still do not have these simple needs met today. Now, deep into the 21st century, I return to those same themes as I close this book, but with a different lens: one that more fully comprehends that our human bonds must expand to recognize our entangled lives with animals.

We, as humans, will never have the oxygen we need to live our lives completely until we recognize that we too are animals: we share the air, water, and land with other species. The United Nations Intergovernmental Panel on Climate Change's (2021) most recent report, attempts, once again, to alert the world to this inalterable reality: for the planet to survive, humans must learn to share, not to dominate (Intergovernmental Panel on Climate Change, 2021). It is no longer (if it ever was) hyperbole to reiterate, again, that we humans are an interdependent species, and we cannot physically survive without the earth and other animals. Veterinarians have a critical role to play in helping to bring about this new consciousness, as they remain society's most trusted teachers about animals. They, and all of us, must lean into connection, and into the changes that need to occur in how we live our lives *with* other animals.

There *are* veterinarians, often on the margins of the profession, who recognize that the veterinary profession is capable of speaking out on behalf of animals on the earth. For example, the Australian-based organization VALE (Vets Against Live Export) raises awareness about the two billion animals that are exported on trucks and ships each year, and the immense animal suffering that occurs. Other veterinarians, for example, those affiliated with the U.S.-based Paw Project, are confronting their profession about the ongoing refusal to ban the cruel practice of cat declawing. While its mission and approach is somewhat narrow, the American Holistic Veterinary Medicine Association (www.ahvma.org) also provides a space and voice for veterinarians who are beginning to question some of the fundamental premises of the profession. There are many more who understand but remain silent, either by choice, or because they are too exhausted and depleted to speak.

Change in the veterinary profession, and in veterinary education, has been slow, impeded by a static culture and very real and ever-present economic challenges. Yet, the animals of the planet—including human animals—can no longer wait. It is past time for a new form of love to emerge: it is the only path to the planet's survival.

Like McArthur, I try to find hope, and to end this book on that note. For this study, I find hope in my final number of participants, 18. If you recall from Chapter 3, I started this research study with 20 students. Like any qualitative researcher, I was dismayed and frustrated when two students did not complete all five interviews in the study. Within the limits of what was allowed by my Institutional Review Board and protocol approval I tried, repeatedly, to contact them. Eventually I realized that my attempts were futile, and I would have to accept that 18 students, not 20, completed the entire study as it was designed.

More than two years later, as I corresponded with Jessica Pierce about the foreword to this book, I finally began to understand that 18 is actually a meaningful number for me, just as the shard of plexiglass inscribed with the word "oxygen" was symbolic for McArthur. I was raised in the Jewish culture and faith, and the number 18 (or Chai, the Hebrew letters chet and yud) symbolizes life. In the end, that is what I choose to take from this book: life, and its endless promise of renewal, oxygen, continued breath, and change. יה

NOTES

1 "Violence" is my interpretation, one that clearly would not be shared by most in the veterinary profession. See also Pedersen (2013).
2 "Humane Slaughter" is the authors' term, not mine.

9 A Researcher's Tale
Making Change for Animals

Scientists often have an aversion to what nonscientists say about science.

—Jonas Salk ("Introduction," Latour & Woolgar, 1979)

Questions of borders, of who is "inside" and "outside," and how the boundaries change are at the core of many human structures and processes and are central to the elusive goal of social justice. Most readers will immediately recognize the (small "t") truths here in the context of seemingly intractable social and political issues such as immigration, race, gender, and ability. As I have written about in previous publications (Dolby, 2003) these lines are at once bright and distinct and simultaneously wholly imaginary, for they are of human construction and thus always swaying and unstable.

Those who risk to cross borders take chances in our world, yet that is the most significant way that change happens: when borders are breached and challenged, and that which has been limited to "insiders" sees sunshine. Salk's reflection on the resistance to this process, in the opening epigraph to this chapter, is from his introduction to Latour and Woolgar's (1979) *Laboratory Life*. In the influential study, Latour spends two years as an "inside" outsider as a sociologist in a laboratory. As Latour and Woolgar comment on the societal importance of this study in the broader arc of anthropological and scientific research,

> Since the turn of the century, scores of men and women have penetrated deep forests, lived in hostile climates, and weathered hostility, boredom, and disease in order to gather the remnants of so-called primitive societies. By contrast to the frequency of these anthropological excursions, relatively few attempts have been made to penetrate the intimacy of life among tribes which are much nearer at hand.
>
> (p. 17)

Latour goes on to suggest why the study of groups of scientists is so critical to our world,

> Whereas we now have fairly detailed knowledge of the myths and circumcision rituals of exotic tribes, we remain relatively ignorant of the details of equivalent activity among tribes of scientists, whose work is commonly heralded as having startling, or, at least, extremely significant effects on our civilization.
>
> (p. 17)

DOI: 10.1201/9781003269984-9

Latour's use of both the adjective "exotic" and the noun "tribe" is most certainly dated and problematic. What he captures, however, is that all human endeavors involve patterns of interaction, ceremony, hierarchy, status, cooperation, and conflict.[1]

Most professions remain insulated and relatively closed to observation and critique from those who are outside of its processes of certification and initiation. In part, this is the classic dilemma that a researcher faces when wanting to study "up" instead of "down" (Fine, 1994).

Historically, it has been easy to gain access to populations, subjects, and participants who are poor and vulnerable: they have little education or power to resist, and they are accustomed to constant intrusions on their lives from "well-meaning" social service agencies and social workers, and the ever-present fear of the police and the power of the state. In contrast, to study "up" requires permission and access: the wealthy and well-educated control their own doors and allow very few, if anyone, through. This is certainly true of the professions and their allied professional schools where the fields are passed on to the next generation, with very limited influence from those who are external.

In the past two decades, many professional fields have slowly become more open to research conducted by outsiders, often defined as those without a terminal degree in that field.[2] For example, as I have discussed previously, medicine, and the field of medical education, have started to value the insights of scholars and researchers with PhDs and other degrees, understanding that contributions from other fields can strengthen and enhance medical education and the practices of the profession. However, there are only scattered studies of the veterinary profession and the education of veterinary students from those, like me, without a DVM. Lacking human medicine's prestige and central role in society, veterinary medicine may be particularly concerned about critique and criticism from outside, fearful of changes that may interrupt its precarious status. Medical education is confident in its ability to withstand the gaze of outsiders: veterinary medicine finds itself differently situated, and thus more wary. As a result, Arluke's (1997) plea for increased sociological study of the veterinary profession has gone largely unheeded.

Yet, there are now signs of change, largely related to shifts in how society interacts with and understands its relationship to animals. As fields such as animal studies, critical animal studies, anthrozoology, veterinary humanities, posthumanism, and many others gain increased visibility and influence, it is natural that scholars and researchers would begin to look at the field of veterinary medicine more critically and with increased scrutiny. Outside of the academy, new dynamics and relationships between humans and animals are also drivers of this movement. For example, there are increasing numbers of people who keep animals long considered "farm" or "food" animals as pets: these owners, for example, Derek and Steve, Esther's dads, interact regularly with the veterinary profession, and often find it out of step with the needs of pet pigs, chickens, goats, and cows. Perhaps some of these people are horrified when their pet pig, staying overnight in a large animal hospital, is housed next to a pig who is similar in all ways—except that pig is destined for slaughter. These questions accumulate, slowly and steadily, eventually prompting intense examination of how the veterinary profession plays its part in sets of interlocking institutions and institutional practices that create our societal knowledge about animals. Just as

Latour and Woolgar's scientists create scientific knowledge through their everyday lab practices, the students I studied are part of a professional structure and institution that creates how our society classifies, understands, relates to, and ultimately values animals (Jones, 2003).

Deciding to do a research study on a profession that is not your own is not an easy, nor quick, decision. My story of my research in the veterinary profession, which I describe in the following, has multiple starting points. I first briefly discuss my earlier researcher as an outsider doing research in South African schools in the mid-1990s, and how this experience shaped and allowed me to understand the challenges of doing research that crosses borders. I then turn to my experiences with animals over the past 15 years that created the opportunity for the study I discuss in this book. In this final section of this chapter, I reflect to my own researcher stories from this study, providing glimpses of the real struggles that are always present in qualitative research. Any research that hopes to produce change, and make a difference in the world, is always painful for the researcher. Following Pelias (2015), I have focused in this book on telling "stories that matter" (p. 611). While Pelias concentrates on human stories only, I expand his call to include the importance of telling animal stories. In the end, humans are also animals and animal stories are also ours (Challenger, 2021).

RESEARCHING FROM THE OUTSIDE: DOING ETHNOGRAPHY IN A SOUTH AFRICAN HIGH SCHOOL

The research in this book is not my first study as an outsider. In 1996, I spent a year in a South African high school as an ethnographer, looking at how students in a newly democratic nation negotiated and made sense of race in their daily lives (Dolby, 2001). Before that study, I had spent over a decade learning about South Africa and South Africans. My earliest experiences were with the U.S. anti-apartheid movement in the 1980s, which swept college campuses in the 1980s. I started my involvement in 1984 as an undergraduate student activist, an experience I have discussed in other publications (Dolby, 2012, 2021). After graduating from college in 1986, I worked with a Boston-based foundation, Fund for a Free South Africa (FreeSA), which raised funds to support the African National Congress in its efforts toward liberation and the end of apartheid. Through my involvement with FreeSA I got to know and worked with dozens of South Africans—mostly exiles, some students, some other immigrants. Over several years, I became a part of that extended community in the Greater Boston area.

I left my position at FreeSA in the late 1980s to return to graduate school. Through my time working there, I had not been able to travel to South Africa because of apartheid and the ongoing boycott of the country. Given my public history of anti-apartheid activism and support for the liberation movement, it is doubtful that I would have been approved for a visa even if I had applied. All of that changed in 1991, when Nelson Mandela was freed from prison and the country started moving toward free and democratic elections. By the end of 1991, I was in South Africa for the first time, staying with friends in the Johannesburg area and traveling throughout the country (see Dolby, 2021a, for discussion). Multiple trips followed. South Africa in the early 1990s was full of intoxicating possibilities of change. I wandered the streets of Johannesburg alone and with friends for hours day and night, knowing that I was not South African, but feeling comfortable and at home, more so than I did in the United States at that time.

In 1996, I was in a PhD program at the University of Illinois at Urbana-Champaign and was awarded a Fulbright for an ethnographic study of a high school in Durban. I had originally planned and organized to study a school in the Johannesburg area. However, in the intervening years, the security situation in Johannesburg had becoming concerning, and my partner (now husband) was from the Durban area. I spent the (U.S.) summer of 1995 in Durban, visiting dozens of schools to find one that I could use for my research the following year. I was also immersed in the Indian community in Chatsworth, where my husband's family is from and where many of them still live. At the time, South Africa had only recently opened after the end of apartheid, and residential areas were still segregated. During those months, I never met another American, and saw very few other white people, except in the schools I visited, which all had multiracial student populations and predominantly white teachers and administrators.

By the time I started my research in a school I call "Fernwood" in early 1996, I had made approximately ten trips to South Africa. I had been immersed in South African communities and politics for 12 years. I often felt great relief and comfort when I made it to the boarding gate of a South African Airways flight leaving the United States and bound for Johannesburg. Even though I was still, quite obviously, an outsider to the South African experience, particularly the experiences of people who had been marginalized, oppressed, and denied basic human rights under apartheid, I still identified with the people, the struggle, and the land. Watching the outline of the African continent appear from 40,000 feet above did, and still does, bring me happiness.

A year in a working-class school in Durban exposed me to the quotidian realities of everyday people's lives. On many of my early trips to South Africa, I had been immersed in communities that were political, attending meetings, funerals (which were, at the time, political events in South Africa), visiting rural and urban projects that supported emergent artists, writers, actors, and musicians. The students I met a Fernwood, and their communities and parents, were not political activists, but everyday people trying to survive. This was again another divide that I had to negotiate, as the students I spent time with every day knew little to nothing about South African history and the struggle against apartheid, in part because of the apartheid regime's control of history curriculum. I was an outsider who "knew" more than those who had grown up in South Africa, a difficult position to inhabit.

My long, slow process of learning about, traveling in, and finally doing research in South Africa taught me the value of being humble as a researcher, and knowing that to do research that is meaningful, extended immersion in a community before starting a project is invaluable. Of course, this is not always possible. Travel takes time, money, and resources that many people do not have. The pressures of finishing a dissertation, finding an academic position, and working toward promotion and tenure on a fixed clock restrains many researchers from fully being able to explore the context of their research. As a research community our collective scholarship is weaker because of that, but it is only structural changes that can create new terrain that allows for this careful, deliberate approach.

When I started my research on schools in South Africa in the 1990s, I did so, in part, because there were few, if any, full-length, published research studies on desegregated schools. I had spent many hours, over multiple trips, in the libraries at South African universities, reading and copying dissertations and theses that (at that time) were only available there, on microfiche. I had scoured South African university bookstores and purchased every book on desegregated schools and met with many of the researchers. So many of them were kind and generous with their time and shared resources with me. I remember Crain Soudien coming into his office at the University of Cape Town during the summer holidays in January 1992 just to meet with me, because I was only in Cape Town for a few days. He handed me a photocopied packet of readings from one of his courses—a precious gift in 1992—and wished me the best.

Through years of preliminary research, I was convinced that there was a story in South Africa that needed to be told in that moment of transition between apartheid and democracy, and if I did not do it, the possibility may vanish. I told the story of Fernwood not to produce a definitive, canonical work, but to preserve—as much as possible given my lens as an outsider—a moment of time that other researchers could build on, improve, and expand. There are moments that as outsiders we can and should act: particularly at times of immense transition and upheaval, when a sliver of time and place will fade and then vanish, and we may be the only person available to capture that moment where the old disappears and the new emerges.

Like my dissertation research, this project comes out of that sense of urgency, but not without many years of both academic and personal experiences that have informed and shaped my perspectives. The research that this book is based on began in the fall of 2004, when a cat named Rusty decided that he wanted to move into our new home in Lafayette, Indiana. A decade later, I began to feel that I had enough knowledge, experience, and comfort with the world of animals and veterinary medicine to be able to start a research study. I knew I would once again be negotiating the lines between "us" and "them" as an outsider to a project I cared about deeply. I knew it would be, once again, be a struggle, and that the resulting work may be met with mixed emotions by the insiders. As with my earlier research in South Africa, I hope to crack open a space for others to fill with their insights, and to widen and expand the conversation about veterinary medicine and our society's changing relationship with animals.

CROSSING DIFFERENT BORDERS: SEEING ANIMALS

I have written previously about the story of Rusty, and how meeting him opened new possibilities for me and eventually for my research (Dolby, 2012). When we moved to Lafayette in the summer of 2004, we rented (and eventually bought) a home near the downtown area, hidden on a windy road that cut through a ravine. Our neighbors across the street were somewhat reclusive, but they had a friendly, persistent cat named Rusty. Rusty visited us that summer and fall, and eventually decided he would move in with us. Our neighbors, whom we later got to know, had many cats, and Rusty wanted all the attention for himself. At the time, I knew absolutely nothing about cats. I do not think I had even picked up one in my entire life. Yet, when Rusty snuggled into my lap and purred, I felt an immediate connection. Within a few years, I had started volunteering at our local humane society with my neighbor (Rusty's "other mom") Connie. At that time, in 2008, Connie had multiple sclerosis that was quickly progressing. She had been involved in the humane society for decades as a board member and wanted to continue to volunteer. Yet, MS was taking her strength, and she needed help to be able to work directly with animals. Once a week, for what ended up being 12 years until Connie's death in December 2020, I joined her at the shelter and got cats out of cages for her, so that she could brush them. As I became more comfortable there, I started volunteering for additional shifts and duties without Connie. Eventually, my daughter began to join me: by age 5, she had been there two years, and was becoming very knowledgeable about cats and animal shelters.

As a qualitative researcher and an ethnographer, I started to watch and to listen. I carefully observed and interacted with animals, at that point, almost exclusively cats.[3] Using what I now know to be the tools of cognitive ethology, I learned to balance the individual cat in front of me with the species "feline." Eventually I took over writing the cat descriptions that were posted on the outside of cats' cages to entice potential adopters. Every Friday morning, for five years, I wrote 10–12 descriptions of cats: approximately 3000 descriptions over that time. Driving to the animal shelter early on Fridays, I often thought that it would be boring. What new could I possibly discover about cats from description of cat # 2364 that would be different from the two thousand plus that had come before? And yet, as I was reminded thousands and thousands of times, each cat I met was an individual. I did not particularly like or love each cat I met. Contrary to what people think, if you volunteer at an animal shelter long enough, you realize that you do *not* want to take every animal home. But I learned, through repetition and experience, how to see each cat as the individual he or she was.[4]

I also began to work with the public at the shelter. Over the years, I helped potential adopters, families who were simply spending a rainy Saturday afternoon looking at cats, people who were there to donate or search the stray area for a lost cat, and people who had recently just had a beloved pet die. Often not ready to adopt yet, they were at the shelter to grieve in a place where they knew their strong emotions over the loss of their family member would be respected. Every person there had a story: over 12 years, I witnessed many endings and more beginnings.

As I have written about elsewhere, I eventually began to take my newly developed perspectives on the role of animal in our lives and look more critically at the practices in my core field of multicultural education. In 2015, I published a short essay, "Flint's Story: Education and Justice for Animals" (Dolby, 2015a). In the essay, I reflected on a moment in the animal shelter many years previously, as I found myself petting a cat named Flint through the bars on his cage, and reading his intake form, which indicated that he had been tossed out of a car speeding down a nearby road. I wrote,

The person who threw Flint out of a car could easily have been one of my former or present students: nowhere in my syllabus, or in any education course I knew of, would a student be exposed to fundamental principles of respect, empathy, and compassion for animals.

(2015a, n.p.)

Outside of the shelter, I began to explore the scholarship and research in animal studies and was particularly intrigued by the emergent research on empathy, which led to my 2012 book connecting multicultural education to what I then termed the "new empathy." Of course, the field of cognitive ethology was also fascinating, as I quickly saw the parallels between that field's focus on animal stories and qualitative researchers' efforts to tell human ones.

As I became more deeply involved in the animal shelter and rescue community both locally and nationally, I also started to think about possibilities to extend what I was learning into my teaching and research. As an educator, of course I was often drawn to trying to understand the *what, how* and *why* of human–animal interaction. I started asking basic questions about where human knowledge came from, where the evidence was to support that knowledge base, and how the larger societal structures also acted as pedagogical forces. I watched and wrote about change at the interface of animals and society and saw how activism began to change on the ground practices. For example, I have written about the *Paw Project* and their work stopping the inhumane practice of cat declawing (Dolby, 2015). From my vantage point at an animal shelter, I could see how the societal change, precipitated in large part by the *Paw Project*'s efforts, filtered down to shape the attitudes of the entry level kennel staff. When I started volunteering in 2008, there was almost zero awareness of the concerns about declawing among regular staff—many of them would have happily and innocently recommended declawing or taken their own cats to a local vet for the procedure. In contrast, during one of my last shifts 12 years in 2020, I overheard staff denying a potential adopter because the person had indicated on their application that they intended to declaw the cat. Clearly, there was power in being able to shape public and professional attitudes toward animals: the ripple effects were everywhere.

My final steps toward writing this book happened after I had been at the animal shelter for about five years. Through my volunteer efforts, I began to create more connections with the animal side of my campus. After a local newspaper published an op-ed I wrote about animal shelters, I was asked to join Purdue's Institutional Animal Care and Use Committee (IACUC). Federal regulations require that IACUC includes one member who has a PhD (or other terminal degree) but is not a "scientist." Thus, I was the "non-scientist" on the committee, a questionable (at best) demarcation that echoes back to Salk's epigraph at the beginning of this chapter. My three-year term on the IACUC was emotionally and personally difficult, as I have detailed in two published articles (2017a, 2018). Yet, the experience was also extraordinary, as I had the opportunity to get to know and understand animal scientists as complex and real humans. I read thousands of protocols using animal subjects, attended monthly meetings, joined a small group for federally mandated regular inspections of Purdue's animal use facilities throughout Indiana, and participated in subcommittee work. Listening to conversations, both formal within our monthly meetings and more casually during inspection tours (which were many hours and often involved multiple stops using a shared university car) was invaluable background for this research. While I usually disagreed with my colleague's views on animal use in research—after all, unlike me, they *were* animal scientists—as a requirement of my commitment to the IACUC I had to listen to their perspectives and experiences.⁵ This allowed me a small window into seeing the world as they did. During meetings, I frequently listened to conversations about how they saw the role of public attitudes and values in shaping their work. Often, they would justify or defend their invasive research with animals because it was what the public wanted: whether it was a constant supply of steak or new pharmaceuticals. As a trained journalist and a long-time educator, I realized that public education can and does have an effect—not solely on animal shelter staff, as in the case of cat declawing, but on the scientists themselves.

At most monthly IACUC meetings, there would be an update on the activities of animal rights organizations, particularly on recently submitted requests for information under the 1967 Freedom of Information Act (FOIA). Reaction around the table during these brief presentations and discussions was often mixed. Most of the researchers present had built their careers on invasive research on animals: they often had multi-million-dollar grants and employees that depended on the continuation of this type of research. Yet, others felt and expressed that the work that they were doing reflected the public will: if the public changed their priorities, they would follow. I also discovered that even though a vital part of our research, pharmaceutical, and multiple other industries, the work of the IACUC was often invisible. Most of my colleagues in the field of education were unaware that IACUC even existed: when I would mention to others in my college that I was serving a term on Purdue's IACUC, I would largely be met with quizzical looks. Navigating Institutional Review Boards (IRBs) and familiarity with the ethics of human research were of course common terrain for social science and educational researchers, but most were not even aware that there was a parallel structure on our campus (and every campus) for approval for research with animals.

In addition to my invitation to join the IACUC, my volunteer experiences at the animal shelter also led to an early research project in a veterinary school, which was an important precursor to this study. Co-authored with the shelter animal medicine faculty member at my own institution's veterinary college, the survey-based research examined veterinary students' attitudes toward animal welfare and animal rights. The original study design did not include a focus on the concept of animal rights, but students mentioned it so frequently that it was evident that animal rights was also an important, though totally misunderstood, theme. Through the course of that study, I began to realize how little veterinary students knew about both animal welfare and animal rights. As I became more familiar with the veterinary education literature, I also realized its limits, and the ways in which most of the literature (with some notable exceptions, e.g., Rollin) avoided the internal ethical conflicts inherent to the profession. The core questions of this book, about veterinary students' changing relationships with animals and humans through their veterinary education, evolved from this earlier research.

I started this research project in 2015, convinced that there were huge gaps in the veterinary education literature, and that there was an absolute need for longitudinal research and for research from scholars outside of the veterinary profession. Through reading the deep and diverse literature on medical education, I wondered why veterinary education had been overlooked for so long, and I recognized that there were essential conversations about society and animals that remained largely unexplored. As I started to conceptualize and begin my research, the field of veterinary humanities began to take formation. I see this book is an early contribution that to field. In addition, through the research project discussed in this book, I continue to work to forge stronger links with my own field of education, a conversation that I began in my previous (2012) publication, *Rethinking Multicultural Education: The New Empathy and Social Justice*.

STORIES FROM THE OUTSIDE/INSIDE: LISTENING AND WITNESSING

Much like my research in South African high school more than 25 years ago, I come to this study as an outsider, but an outsider who has spent many years in close proximity to the "inside" perspective. Yet, my desire is not to reify these lines of division, but to complicate and disrupt them. In my 2012 book, I explored the emergent science of empathy, trying to investigate ways to break down what some may refer to as the "speciesism" (Ryder, 1970; Singer, 1975) that is endemic to the research in education. I argued that the field should be re-centered around the concept of empathy, following Lecky (1869) and Singer (1997), to include non-human animals. It was, and is, my belief that education is intellectually a stronger practice when we open to new perspectives and ways of being in the world: that crossing self-constructed professional borders leads to important collaborations and ways of making change. Since the publication of that book in 2012, there has been a steady increase in educational research and scholarship from a critical, multi-species, and interspecies perspective, as I discussed earlier in Chapter 2. In 2012, I wrote toward the field of education opening to new and different ways of understanding the human/non-human animal relationship. Now, I write to attempt to open up conversations within veterinary education, and to demonstrate how the field can be enriched, changed, and challenged through re-imagining the human/non-human relationships that shape its philosophical and ethical compass.

As a researcher, much of what I did through the course of this study was to listen and to witness. Often, what I heard and sometimes saw, was very difficult. As an example, the following is an excerpt between Michelle and I from our final interview in 2019. Michelle was reflecting on a clinical rotation that she had at the beginning of her fourth year on ruminant production. As is sometimes common with field-based courses, once students are out of town with their course professor, there will be detours and stops at farms and other animal facilities that may (or may not) be clearly related to the specific topic of that rotation. In this case, Michelle and her classmates stopped at a deer and elk farm where the farmer also kept a pet bear,

Michelle: Yesterday, we went out with the elk and the deer, and he also had a pet bear. You want to see a picture of it? (pulls out phone to show me)
Nadine: A pet bear?
Michelle: I'm not joking. A bear. A pet bear. I was shocked.
Nadine: Okay.
Michelle: I know. This guy was interesting, and I think you kind of have to be a little interesting to have a pet bear. If he—

Nadine: How much of a pet is the bear?

Michelle: Oh, it's friendly. It's tame. I refused to go in with it. I was like, "I'm not." And he told us—he's like, "You have to be careful" because, I mean, you never know. This thing can turn, and he's had it for 11 years.

Nadine: Okay.

Michelle: And I was like, "I'm not going in there with that bear. I don't care how tame [laughter] you say it is. I'm not going to risk my life now because of a pet bear." But he was really interesting. He definitely had a huge bond with all of his animals, and even though—with the bear, he could pet the bear. But with the elk and all the deer, he couldn't physically interact with them. He didn't pet them or anything because they were wild, but he has them in a huge, fenced-in enclosure.

Nadine: What does he do with them?

Michelle: So what he does is he raises them and then sells them to hunting preserves because I guess you can get huge amounts of money, like $12,000 depending on the size of their rack. And I had no idea that market even existed, and so that was an eye-opener. . . . And so it was really interesting just to dart them and then see them go down and then you have a good amount of time to work on them until you give them a reversal. And then they would pop right back up like nothing even happened. That was cool cause I never had an experience like that. So it was neat.

Kiara told me about a similar experience, but this time on a university sponsored study abroad trip to Thailand. Here, I excerpt some of our conversation about a tiger park,

Kiara: We went to a tiger park. And I guess to my understanding is that the owner opened it not so much to preserve the tigers as to make money. So they had people taking pictures of them, and they were in cages and stuff like that. They were pretty big cages, but they are pretty solitary animals, and some of them were housed two at a time, three at a time. And then we went to a retirement center with the older tigers, and they were like individually housed in smaller areas. And some of us were debating, is that right, should we even be taking pictures of the tigers, despite them being treated very well, they were fed very well. It's the rainy season, so they weren't able to let them out as much, because some of their property was damaged, so just to see them pacing back and forth and distressed. Some of us were, ah, I don't know if this is right. Yeah, they're being treated well, but they shouldn't be living like this. And some other people were, no, it's fine, they're being treated well, that's all that matters, it's okay. Just seeing that difference in how everybody felt, that was an awkward and tense situation for all of us.

Nadine: And what did you think?

Kiara: I thought they were being treated very well. The reason behind the whole tiger park may not be the best. I mean, I wouldn't want to be kept in a cage or in housing just to make somebody money. But I felt like they were being treated very well, they were housed very well, the caretakers were treating them, like they weren't being rude to them, they weren't hurting them, so I didn't necessarily see a problem.

Nadine: Did you see a welfare issue?

Kiara: Not necessarily. I feel like the housing was appropriate, it was appropriate sized housing, they were given enrichment, they were given food and water, and then they were being let out when they could be let out—unfortunately because of the whole storm, I'm not sure. But at the end of the day, they could be showing us one thing, and then when we leave, they could be totally rude and mean to these animals. So it's hard to say. But I didn't see a welfare problem, at least one that was alarming to me.

Nadine: Did the tigers pacing back and forth concern you?

Kiara: I know some of them, they were like, they're playful, you know, they want to come out. That was a little concerning, because they need space to roam, especially those that were in retirement, they were in smaller caging compared to those at the park, it was kind of like, ah, I hope they let them out, despite everything going on, if it doesn't rain, they can let them out a little longer than they usually do. That was a little bit like ah, I hope that they were able to roam and be free.

Nadine: The professor that went with you, how did he talk about it with you?

Kiara: He kind of left it up to our interpretation. He kind of saw the pros and cons as well. We were grateful for the opportunity to learn because the Thai veterinarian pulled strings because she knew someone who worked there. So we were grateful in order to be able to see that, but at the same time, He said, I'm going to stay out of it, but take it as you will.

Not surprisingly, these interviews were emotionally draining for me, as I tried to sleep, but instead was continually haunted by images of bears and tigers—wild animals—held captive. The elk and deer, too, were captive, as they were bred to be sold to canned hunting facilities with no chance of escape. Most troubling, of course, was that students encountered these animals through their veterinary education classes and clinical field experiences, and that the faculty involved implicitly sanctioned and approved this abuse through the act of normalizing it. One cannot "stay out of it" when witnessing such clear animal abuse. Yet, this is exactly what the students heard from the faculty member with them at the Thai tiger park. Michelle never mentions the faculty member who was with her at the deer and elk farm raising any concerns about the bear being held in a cage, nor animal welfare issues related to the raising of deer and elk for canned hunting. Michelle was even invited to go into the cage with the pet bear, though wisely made the decision to decline.

Often, I heard the students simply chuckle about eccentric faculty: the ethical issues that are directly in front of them are ignored and attributed to "Professor so and so" who does strange things on the side. In my interview with Michelle, she extends this way of thinking to understanding people who own wild animals, labeling the owner of the bear, and the entire situation as "interesting." While Michelle was concerned enough about the situation to protect her own well-being, and thus not accept the invitation to go into the cage with the bear, she also never openly critiqued the owner. She expressed shock but not outrage. Perhaps in part her reaction is framed through the fact that her visit to the farm and her meeting with the bear was facilitated through a professor and a course in her veterinary curriculum: thus, it was implicitly (and explicitly) sanctioned by her veterinary school and her future profession. This reality paralleled much of what I experienced as a member of my own institution's IACUC, particularly on inspection tours at farms and other research facilities throughout the county and surrounding areas. Distance, closed doors, and insular human cultures create institutional systems where no one "sees" the animal suffering, and it becomes accepted as normal (Gluck, 2016).

THE BEYOND: TELLING STORIES FOR CHANGE

Every interview I had with students over the five years of this research study raised ethical issues around animals, ones which I, as a (knowledgeable and informed) outsider to the profession could clearly see. The multiple conversations I had with Kiara about the kitten research were particularly intense and memorable, as she struggled with her underlying feelings of attachment to the kittens, and her conflicted loyalty to the profession she was entering. Even when I told her, years later, that there had been a public outcry and the research had been halted, she had mixed emotions, feeling torn about the contradictory imperatives of her emotional ties to the kittens and the profession. Kiara had fully internalized, by this point, that it was normal for veterinarians to have these feelings. As an outsider to the profession, I felt dismayed and distressed that Kiara had come to accept these feelings as routine and acceptable. Kiara's story, of course is reminiscent of Marissa's that I discussed in Chapter 6: Marissa accepts that as a veterinarian she will always have anxiety, and Kiara accepts that she will always witness and be part of animal suffering and pain.

As a researcher, I could only listen. I longed to tell Marissa, Kiara, and the other students, all of them struggling with how to retain and redefine their humanity through this journey, that there are other possible paths forward for the veterinary profession. And, of course, I fervently wished that they had the opportunity through their veterinary education to have these conversations, to raise these concerns, and to advocate for change within their college and their profession. But overwhelmingly the students in my study were not in a position nor inclined to do this: they had taken on considerable debt to complete their veterinary education, and simply desired to check the boxes on coursework and required clinical experiences. They did not have skills of critical analysis and thinking from their undergraduate education that would have allowed them to do this. Sadly, if they had acquired the ability to raise difficult, ethical questions during their undergraduate education, they may have concluded that that the veterinary profession was too emotionally and morally challenging for them to be comfortable continuing on that path. With no ethical framework or opportunity to reflect seriously on what they saw, the pet bear, caged tiger, sick and suffering kittens, and other abused animals they would encounter through veterinary school would remain oddities: stories they might tell late at night as they remembered their own hazing, suffering, and ultimate survival. Acceptance and acquiescence to the norms and values of the profession were largely what the students in my study took from their experiences with animals in veterinary school. Change, asking questions, and probing faculty attitudes and practices were not a part of these students' mindset nor experiences. By the time that they graduated in the spring of 2019, they had a complete, if sobering, understanding of the role of animals and humans in the veterinary profession.

If you have read this far, you undoubtedly understand that it is not only the students, but I as a researcher who also now has this complete and sobering understanding. Veterinarians and the veterinary profession are a part of my daily life. I live in a multi-species (Irvine & Cilia, 2017; Laurent-Simpson, 2021) family with several cats (Orie, Pizzazz, Gus, and sometimes Otis), and one dog (Eddie). I am the president of a local non-profit, Animal Advocates of Greater Lafayette, which works to change keep pets out of animal shelters and keep families together through supporting them with the daily financial expenses of pet care. The organization also works on a broader level to change attitudes toward animals and the human–animal relationship. Veterinarians, and the veterinary profession are key partners in these conversations and in making these changes.

The stories I tell in this book about the students' journeys through veterinary school, and my own journey with them, are—I hope—part of this change. There is no question that the veterinary profession is facing enormous challenges, both internally and externally. Unlike human medicine, there is no insurance or social safety net for animals. Even the United States, with its sparse social supports, has human programs such as Medicare and Medicaid, along with the Affordable Care Act, passed during the Obama administration in 2010. While there are limited pet insurance programs, legal owners of animals must pay for the veterinary care that their animals, whether cherished pet or destined for the dinner table, receive. Homeless animals, wildlife, and countless other species and types of animals only receive care through government and non-profit organizations.

Thus, while the stories I relate are veterinary stories, the solutions and the change must come from all of us who care about animals as both beloved companions and critical links in the natural world. The questions I raise about how veterinarians should be educated, what they should and should not actually do, and the complicated ethical issues they face are not solely for the veterinary profession to solve. Animals belong to all of us. They are not outside us as humans, because we are also animals. We are united in a common need for oxygen, to breathe, and to love. These are the new stories that I hope another researcher hears from veterinary students 20 years hence: that a renewed recognition of what we share as animals has led to at least the beginning of a transformation, and a more humane education and world for all of "we animals" (McArthur, 2017).

NOTES

1 "Exotic" is a term that is used to other and to distance, and "tribe," except in reference to federally recognized Native American tribes in the United States, is also, in 2022, understood as a term that is used to separate and demean (Lowe, 2001). I use the quote because Latour and Woolgar, like Miner (1956) turns the colonialist, Western gaze around, to focus on self. Many years ago, when I lived in Melbourne, Australia, the newly opened

Melbourne Museum had an exhibit that featured the statue of a white man, an anthropologist, encased in glass. The exhibit forced visitors to confront the reality that the "scientist" himself (in this case) is not omniscient, but is also positioned, and is also object. Latour and Woolgar no doubt realize the racism and xenophobia inherent here, as they refer to "so-called primitive societies."

2 Borders and boundaries are never clearly defined and static. For example, researchers and academics make distinctions between "clinical" and "tenure-line" faculty, and further distinctions within faculty themselves dependent on rank (e.g., in the United States, assistant, associate, and full professor). So, for example, an article published by a clinical veterinary faculty member may be viewed differently in terms of "inside/outside" than one published by a full professor.

3 Because of Connie's physical limitations, she could only volunteer in the cat area, so I remained there with her. Several years later, my then preschool daughter was very scared of the loud barking in the dog area, and thus with her also, I remained in the cat area. Because of these two personal circumstances, I volunteered almost exclusively with cats at the animal shelter, though I did complete the introductory volunteer training for dogs.

4 My experience writing individual descriptions of cats for five years was the inspiration for the "Day in the Life" assignment that I have used in my classes on Animals, Society, and Education. For discussion of the class and the assignment, which draws on the principles of cognitive ethnology, see Dolby (2017).

5 This was not my first time interacting with lab animal scientists. One of my first jobs after graduating from Boston University in 1986 was with Public Responsibility in Medicine and Research (PRIMR), which had been founded in 1973 in the Boston area, and was one of the first U.S. organizations to provide education and training for researchers subject to IRB and IACUC protocols and regulations. The National Research Act of 1974, and amendments to the Animal Welfare Act in 1986 created the groundwork for greater federal regulation in the area of protection of human and animal subjects. PRIMR in 1986 was extremely tiny (when I started, I was the only employee). By 2022, it has grown to an organization with over 20 employees, an expansive board of directors, and a worldwide footprint.

Coda

On a sweltering August afternoon, just as I was finishing the manuscript for this book, I found myself in the lobby of the small animal hospital at my own institution, with my dog in my lap.

Eddie has had many health problems since we adopted him from a local rescue in February 2020. This time, he needed to see a veterinary ophthalmologist for a serious eye issue: so here we were.

I sat in the lobby—just recently re-opened to clients after the COVID shutdown, for almost 90 minutes, while Eddie was seen by a surgeon, examined, evaluated, and his eye was biopsied. I had heard from colleagues that the patient volume at the small animal hospital had increased an astounding 80% during the shutdown. While I cannot vouch for the accuracy of that number, the crush of people and pets in the lobby that day was overwhelming. During the time, I was in the lobby, I witnessed a constant stream of patients—I counted more than 30 dogs and cats in that short window. There were multiple traumas: puppies not breathing, cats with broken legs, simply an endless flow. The lobby was so full of people that when I left for a few minutes to go into the exam room with Eddie, I came back to find nowhere to sit. It was astonishing to me, in part because I was there mid-afternoon, while dozens of veterinary practices all over my community were open and seeing patients, though I knew that many were booked solid for weeks. Demand for veterinary services is unprecedented in my area, as I know it is throughout the United States right now.

Amidst all this chaos were the doctors, nurses, residents, interns, veterinary students, and staff who stoically and deliberately treated each patient, and communicated complex medical information to each human client. The dogs were cute (the cats were in carriers, I am sure they were cute too!), but it was the humans who were my focus.

The enormous stressors facing the veterinary profession were on display that hot afternoon. They kept up with the constant flow of people, pets, and emergencies, but clearly just barely. I also suspected that I was not there at the height of the rush: what happened then? Many of the people in the lobby appeared to have adequate financial resources to pay for the astronomical bills. I overheard the receptionists taking credit cards and ringing up totals: $2100, $1700, $575. Other clients who appeared less wealthy were ushered into private rooms, most likely for frank, if kind, conversations about the costs involved in medical care at an elite veterinary hospital. Were their pets euthanized? Surrendered? Only treated with the most basic of care and released?

I wondered about the internal, hidden pressures and anxieties that surrounded me. The people who buzzed around the lobby and exam rooms were, of course, not the participants in my study. Yet, they were part of the same profession, and many—if not most—had been through a similar, if not identical, veterinary education. What had it done to them, to their humanity, to their connections and disconnections to other humans, and to animals? Had they thrived? Had they crumbled? What did their faces look like when they turned away from me, a client? These same questions haunt me every time I go to my local veterinary practices (we use two in town).

As Jessica Pierce reflected in the foreword, I was witnessing "mission impossible," a profession facing cross-cutting, simultaneous emergencies. Will veterinary education and the profession change over the next decades? If so, how? I can only hope that the often raw, unfiltered, and sometimes painful conversations that I had with the veterinary students in this study, which are at the core of this book, can contribute to creating openings for more talk and reflection.

Because for myself, as I sat in the lobby, amidst the chaos, what I felt most of all was love. Love for the animals, but even more than that, love for the people. It would have been easy to feel despair, disappointment, and maybe anger. But I did not. I felt love, gratitude, and the hope and promise of what may come next.

References

Abood, S., & Siegford, J. (2012). Student perceptions of an animal-welfare and ethics course taught early in the veterinary curriculum. *Journal of Veterinary Medical Education, 39*(2), 136–141.

Adams, R. (2011, March 6). Narrative's medicine. *The Chronicle of Higher Education, 57*(35), B20.

Allen, C., & Bekoff, M. (1997). *Species of mind: The philosophy and biology of cognitive ethology.* Cambridge, MA: The MIT Press.

Altan, S., & Lane, J. (2018). Teachers' narratives: A source for exploring the influences of teachers' significant life experiences on their dispositions and teaching practices. *Teaching and Teacher Education, 74,* 238–248.

American Pet Product Association. (2021). *Pet industry market size and owner statistics.* Retrieved from www.americanpetproducts.org

American Veterinary Medical Association. (2020, December 10). *Pet populations are on the way up.* Retrieved from www.avma.org

American Veterinary Medical Association. (2020a). *2020 economic state of the veterinary profession.* Schaumburg, IL: Author.

American Veterinary Medical Association. (2020b, December 3). *Veterinary labor demand remains strong during COVID.* Retrieved from www.avma.org

American Veterinary Medical Association. (2021). *U.S. pet ownership statistics.* Retrieved from www.avma.org/resources-tools/reports-statistics/us-pet-ownership-statistics

American Veterinary Medical Association. (2021a). *Human-animal bond.* Retrieved from avma.org

American Veterinary Medical Association. (2021b). *Animal welfare: What is it?* Retrieved from avma.org

Apple, M. (1979). *Ideology and curriculum.* New York: Routledge.

Arbour, R., Signal, T., & Taylor, N. (2009). Teaching kindness: The promise of humane education. *Society & Animals, 17,* 136–148.

Arkow, P. (2020). Human—animal relationships and social work: Opportunities beyond the veterinary environment. *Child and Adolescent Social Work Journal, 37,* 573–588.

Arluke, A. (1997). Veterinary education: A plea and plan for sociological study. *Anthrozoös, 10,* 3–7.

Arluke, A. (2004). The use of dogs in medical and veterinary training: Understanding and approaching student uneasiness. *Journal of Applied Animal Welfare Science, 7*(3), 197–204.

Arluke, A., & Hafferty, F. (1996). From apprehension to fascination with "dog lab": The use of absolution by medical students. *Journal of Contemporary Ethnography, 25*(2), 201–225.

Armitage-Chan, E., & May, S. A. (2019). The veterinary identity: A time and context model. *Journal of Veterinary Medical Education, 46*(2), 153–162.

Association of American Veterinary Colleges. (2015). *50 & forward: Celebrating 50 years of public service, 1996–2016.* Washington, DC: Author.

Association of American Veterinary Colleges. (2020, October 16). *Number of applicants to veterinary medical colleges soars 19 percent year-over-year.* Retrieved from www.aavmc.org/news/

Association of Professional Humane Educators. (2021). *About APHE.* Retrieved from www.aphe.org/about-aphe

Axworthy, N. (2019, June 28). *Esther the Wonder Pig fans outraged by university pig roast.* *Veg News.* Retrieved from vegnews.com

Balmer, D., & Richards, B. (2017). Longitudinal qualitative research in medical education. *Perspectives in Medical Education, 6,* 306–310.

Bamber, M., Allen-Collinson, J., & McCormack, J. (2017). Occupational limbo, transitional liminality and permanent liminality: New conceptual distinctions. *Human Relations, 70*(12), 1514–1537.

Barr, G., & Herzog, H. (2000). Fetal pig: The high school dissection experience. *Society & Animals, 8*(1), 53–69.

Barron, D., Khosa, D., & Jones-Bitton, A. (2017). Experiential learning in primary care: Impact on veterinary students' communication confidence. *Journal of Experiential Education, 40*(4), 349–365.

Bekoff, M. (2000). *The smile of a dolphin: Remarkable accounts of animal emotions.* New York: Discovery Books.

Bekoff, M. (2006). Animal passions and beastly virtues: Cognitive ethology as the unifying science for understanding the subjective, emotional, empathic, and moral lives of animals. *Zygon, 41*(1), 71–104.

Bekoff, M. (2007). *The emotional lives of animals.* Novato, CA: New World Library.

Bekoff, M. (2013). *Why dogs hump and bees get depressed.* Novato, CA: New World Library.

Bekoff, M., & Jamieson, D. (1990). Cognitive ethology and applied philosophy: The significance of an evolutionary biology of mind. *TREE, 5*(5), 156–159.

Bekoff, M., & Pierce, J. (2010). *Wild justice: The moral lives of animals.* Chicago: University of Chicago Press.

Bekoff, M., & Pierce, J. (2017). *The animals' agenda: Freedom, compassion, and coexistence in the human age.* Boston: Beacon Press.

Beston, H. (1928). *The outermost house.* New York: Doubleday and Doran.

Blackwell, T., & Rollin, B. (2008). Leading discussions on animal rights. *Journal of the American Veterinary Medical Association, 233*(6), 868–871.

Blum, S. (2016). *'I love learning, I hate school': An anthropology of college.* Ithaca, NY: Cornell University Press.

Boller, E., Courtman, N., Chiavaroli, N., & Beck, C. (2021). Design and delivery of the clinical integrative puzzle as a collaborative learning tool. *Journal of Veterinary Medical Education, 48*(2), 150–157.

Bone, J. (2013). The animal as fourth educator: A literature review of animals and young children in pedagogical relationships. *Australasian Journal of Early Childhood, 38*(2), 57.

Bones, V. C., & Yeates, J. W. (2012). The emergence of veterinary oaths: Social, historical, and ethical considerations. *Journal of Animal Ethics, 2*(1), 20–42.

Breier, M., Herman, C., & Towers, L. (2020). Doctoral rites and liminal spaces: Academics without PhDs in South Africa and Australia. *Studies in Higher Education, 45*(4), 834–846.

Brown, H., & Nading, A. (2019). Introduction: Human animal health in medical anthropology. *Medical Anthropology Quarterly, 33*(1), 5–23.

Bruhn, S., & Jimenez, R. (2020). Portraiture as a method of inquiry in educational research. *Harvard Educational Review, 90*(1), 49–53.

Burns, G., Ruby, K., DeBowes, R., Seaman, S., & Brennan, J. (2006). Teaching non-technical (professional) competence in a veterinary school curriculum. *Journal of Veterinary Medical Education, 33*(2), 301–308.

Caplow, S., & Thomsen, J. (2019). Significant life experiences and animal-themed education. In T. Lloro-Bidart & V. Banschbach (Eds.), *Animals in environmental education: Interdisciplinary approaches to curriculum and pedagogy* (pp. 237–257). Cham, Switzerland: Palgrave-Macmillan.

Capucilli, A. S. (2008). *Biscuit visits the doctor.* New York: HarperFestival.

Challenger, M. (2021). *How to be an animal: A new history of what it means to be human.* New York: Penguin Books.

Chalwa, L. (1998). Research methods to investigate significant life experiences: Review and recommendations. *Environmental Education Research, 4*(4), 383–397.

Chan, S. (2016, March 17). *SeaWorld says it will end breeding of killer whales.* Retrieved from www.nytimes.com

Channon, S. B., Davis, R. C., Goode, N. T., & May, S. A. (2017). What makes a "good group"? Exploring the characteristics and performance of undergraduate student groups. *Advances in Health Sciences Education: Theory and Practice, 22*(1), 17–41.

Charon, R. (2001). Narrative medicine: A model for empathy, reflection, profession, and trust. *Journal of the American Medical Association, 286*(15), 1897–1902.

Charon, R. (2006). *Narrative medicine: Honoring the stories of illness.* Oxford: Oxford University Press.

Choplin, L. (2018, November). *World's first habeas corpus order issued on behalf of an elephant.* Retrieved from www.nonhumanrights.org/blog/first-habeas-corpus-order-happy/

Christakis, D. A., & Feudtner, C. (1993). Ethics in a short white coat: The ethical dilemmas that medical students confront. *Academic Medicine, 68*, 249–254.

Colliver, J., Conlee, M., Verhulst, S., & Dorsey, J. (2010). Reports of the decline of empathy during medical education are greatly exaggerated: A reexamination of the research. *Academic Medicine, 85*(4), 588–593.

Colombo, E. S., Pelosi, A., & Prato-Previde, E. (2016). Empathy towards animals and belief in animal-human-continuity in Italian veterinary students. *Animal Welfare, 25*(2), 275–286.

Cron, W. L., Slocum, J. V., Jr, Goodnight, D. B., & Volk, J. O. (2000). Executive summary of the Brakke management and behavior study. *Journal of the American Veterinary Medical Association, 217*(3), 332–338.

Croney, C. (2010). Words matter: Implications of semantics and imagery in framing animal welfare issues. *Journal of Veterinary Medical Education, 37*(1), 101–106.

Croney, C. (2014). Bonding with commodities: Social constructions and implications of human-animal relationships in contemporary livestock production. *Animal Frontiers, 4*(3), 59–64.

Croney, C., & Reynnells, R. (2008). The ethics of semantics: Do we clarify or obfuscate reality to influence perceptions of farm animal production? *Poultry Science, 87*(2), 387–391.

Cushing, M. (2020). *Pet nation: The love affair that changed America.* New York: Avery Books.

Dally, M. (2011). Ethical considerations raised by the provision of freebies to veterinary students. *Journal of the American Veterinary Association, 238*(12), 1551–1554.

Daly, B., & Suggs, S. (2010). Teachers' experiences with humane education and animals in the elementary classroom: Implications for empathy development. *Journal of Moral Education, 39*(1), 101–112.

Damasio, A. (1994). *Descartes' error: Emotion, reason, and the human brain.* New York: Putnam.

Darder, D., Baltodano, M., & Torres, R. (Eds.). (2017). *The critical pedagogy reader* (3rd ed.). New York: Routledge.

Darwin, C. (1871/1998). *The expression of the emotions in man and animals* (3rd ed.). New York: Oxford University Press.

Davis, B., & Sumara, D. (2005). Challenging images of knowing: Complexity science and educational research. *International Journal of Qualitative Studies in Education, 18*(3), 305–321.

DeMello, M. (Ed.). (2012). *Animals and society: An introduction to human-animal studies*. New York: Columbia University Press.

Descartes, R. (1637/1960). *Discourse on method and meditations* (Lafleur, L. J., Trans.). New York: The Liberal Arts Press.

De Waal, F. (2001). *The ape and the sushi master*. New York: Basic Books.

De Waal, F. (2009). *The age of empathy: Nature's lessons for a kinder society*. New York: Harmony Books.

Dickey, B. (2016). *Pit bull: The battle over an American icon*. New York: Vintage Books.

Dolby, N. (2001). *Constructing race: Youth, identity, and popular culture in South Africa*. Albany, NY: SUNY Press.

Dolby, N. (2003). A small place: Jamaica Kincaid and a methodology of connection. *Qualitative Inquiry, 9*(1), 57–73.

Dolby, N. (2012). *Rethinking multicultural education for the next generation: The new empathy and social justice*. New York, NY: Routledge.

Dolby, N. (2015). *The Paw Project*: Animals and education in the public sphere. *Critical Education, 6*(23), 1–14. Retrieved from https://ices.library.ubc.ca/index.php/criticaled/article/view/186000

Dolby, N. (2015a). Flint's story: Education and justice for animals. *Teachers College Record Online*, January.

Dolby, N. (2016). What did your vet learn in school today? The hidden curriculum of veterinary education. In S. Rice & A. G. Rud (Eds.), *The educational significance of human and non-human animal interactions* (pp. 69–86). New York: Palgrave Macmillan.

Dolby, N. (2017). Experiential education in the honors classroom: Animals, society and education. *Honors in Practice, 13*, 71–88.

Dolby, N. (2017a). Animal research in higher education: Engaging the moral and ethical conversation. *Journal of College and Character, 18*(1), 64–69.

Dolby, N. (2018). Animal research on campus: Reflections on my experience in the field. *Educational Studies, 54*(6), 629–640.

Dolby, N. (2019). Nonhuman animals and the future of environmental education: Empathy and new possibilities. *The Journal of Environmental Education, 50*(4–6), 403–415.

Dolby, N. (2020). Learning at noon: Critical teacher education and lunch as curriculum. *Critical Education, 11*(8), 1–16.

Dolby, N. (2020a). Incoming veterinary students' perspectives on animal welfare: A qualitative study. *Journal of Applied Animal Ethics Research, 2*, 1–21.

Dolby, N. (2021). Animals, community, and justice matters in critical times. *International Review of Qualitative Research*. https://doi.org/10. 1177/ 1940 8447 2110 12648

Dolby, N. (2021a). Afterword: Young people and the future of African worlds. In P. Ugor (Ed.), *Youth and popular culture in Africa: Media, music, and politics* (pp. 385–390). Rochester, NY: University of Rochester Press.

Dolby, N., & Dimitriadis, G. (Eds.). (2004). *Learning to labor in new times*. New York: Routledge.

Dolby, N., & Litster, A. (2015). Understanding veterinarians as educators: An exploratory study. *Teaching in Higher Education, 20*(3), 272–284.

Dolby, N., & Litster, A. (2019). Animal welfare and animal rights: An exploratory study of veterinary students' perspectives. *Society & Animals, 27*, 575–594.

Donald, M. (2019). When care is defined by science: Exploring veterinary medicine through a more-than-human geography of empathy. *Area, 51*, 470–487.

Dooley, L., & Makasis, N. (2020). Understanding student behavior in a flipped classroom: Interpreting learning analytics data in the veterinary pre-clinical sciences. *Education Sciences, 10*(10), 260.

Dowers, K. L., Schoenfeld-Tacher, R. M., Hellyer, P. W., & Kogan, L. R. (2015). Corporate influence and conflicts of interest: Assessment of veterinary medical curricular changes and student perceptions. *Journal of Veterinary Medical Education, 42*(1), 1–10.

Drew, C., George, A., Ketenci, S., Lupinacci, J., Nocella, A., Purdy, I., & Schatz, J. (2019). Introduction: Examining the nexus: Critical animal studies and critical pedagogy. In C. Drew et al. (Eds.), *Education for total liberation: Critical animal pedagogy and teaching against speciesism* (pp. 1–12). New York, NY: Peter Lang.

Driscoll, L. (2018). I *want to be a veterinarian*. New York: HarperCollins Publishers.

Ellis, C., & Irvine, L. (2010). Reproducing dominion: Emotional apprenticeship in the 4-H livestock program. *Society & Animals, 18*, 21–39.

English, F. (2000). A critical appraisal of Sarah Lawrence-Lightfoot's *Portraiture* as a method of educational research. *Educational Researcher, 29*(7), 21–26.

Erickson, F., & Gutierrez, K. (2002). Culture, rigor, and science in educational research. *Educational Researcher, 31*(8), 21–24.

Fine, M. (1994). Working the hyphens: Reinventing self and other in qualitative research. In N. R. Denzin & Y. S. Lincoln (Eds.), *Handbook of qualitative research* (pp. 70–82). Thousand Oaks, CA: Sage.

Foer, J. S. (2009). *Eating animals*. New York: Little, Brown, and Company.

Foer, J. S. (2019). *We are the weather: Saving the planet begins at breakfast*. New York: Farrar, Straus & Giroux.

Foucault, M. (1972). *The archaeology of knowledge*. London: Tavistock Publications.

Freidson, E. (2001). *Professionalism: The third logic*. Chicago; University of Chicago Press.

Freire, P. (1970). *Pedagogy of the oppressed* (Ramos, M., Trans.). New York: Continuum International Publishing Group.

Gage, L., & Gage, N. (1993). *If wishes were horses*. New York: St. Martin's Press.

Gardiner, A. (2014). The "dangerous" women of animal welfare: How British veterinary medicine went to the dogs. *Social History of Medicine, 27*(20), 466–487.

Gillespie, K. (2018). *The cow with ear tag #1389*. Chicago: University of Chicago Press.

Giroux, H., & Purpel, D. (Eds.). (1983). *The hidden curriculum and moral education: Deception or discovery?* Berkeley, CA: McCutchan Publishing.

Gluck, J. (2016). *Voracious science & vulnerable animals: A primate scientist's ethical journey*. Chicago: University of Chicago Press.

Goldberg, J. (2008). Humanism or professionalism? The white coat ceremony and medical education. *Academic Medicine, 83*(3), 715–722.

Goodall, J. (2021, March 22). *A joint open letter to the Associated Press calling for a change in animal pronouns-Animals are a who, not a what*. Retrieved from www.idausa.org

Goodman, J. (2018, May 7). *USDA "uses kittens as test tubes"*. Retrieved from https://blog.whitecoatwaste.org/

Gordon, L., Rees, C. E., & Jindal-Snape, D. (2020). Doctors' identity transitions: Choosing to occupy a state of "betwixt and between". *Medical Education, 54*(11), 1006–1018.

Griffin, D. (1976). *The question of animal awareness: Evolutionary continuity of mental experience*. New York: Rockefeller University Press.

Grimm, D. (2014). *Citizen canine: Our evolving relationship with cats and dogs*. New York: PublicAffairs.

Gruen, L. (2015). *Entangled empathy: An alternative ethic for our relationships with animals*. New York: Lantern Books.

Guenther, K. (2020). *The lives and deaths of shelter animals*. Stanford, CA: Stanford University Press.

Hafferty, F. (1991). *Into the valley: Death and the socialization of medical students*. New Haven, CT: Yale University Press.

Hafferty, F. (2009). Professionalism and the socialization of medical students. In R. Cruess, S. Cruess, & Y. Steinert (Eds.), *Teaching medical professionalism* (pp. 53–70). Cambridge: Cambridge University Press.

Hart, L., Wood, M., & Hart, B. (2008). *Why dissection? Animal use in education.* Westport, CT: Greenwood Press.

Hayes, D., & Hayes, G. B. (2015). *Cowed: The hidden impact of 93 million cows on America's health, economy, politics, culture, and environment.* New York: W. W. Norton & Co.

Hazel, S., Signal, T., & Taylor, N. (2011). Can teaching veterinary and animal-sciences students about animal welfare affect their attitude toward animals and human-related empathy? *Journal of Veterinary Medical Education, 38*(1), 74–83.

Hegedus, C., & Pennebaker, D. A. (2016). *Unlocking the cage.* New York: Pennebaker/ Hegedus Films.

Heintzman, K. (2018). A cabinet of the ordinary: Domesticating veterinary education, 1766– 1799. *British Journal for the History of Science, 51*(2), 239–260.

Herbert, S., & Lynch, J. (2017). Classroom animals provide than just science education. *Science & Education, 26,* 107–123.

Herzog, H. (1989). Conversations with veterinary students: Attitudes, ethics, and animals. *Anthrozoös, 2*(3), 181–188.

Herzog, H. (2010). *Some we love, some we hate, some we eat: Why it's so hard to think straight about animals.* New York: HarperCollins Publishers.

Herzog, H. (2011). The impact of pets on human health and psychological well-being: Fact, fiction, or hypothesis? *Current Directions in Psychological Science, 20*(4), 236–239.

Herzog, H. (2020, June 26). *Why has the "pet effect" meme spread so rapidly?* Retrieved from www.psychologytoday.com/us/blog/animals-and-us

Hesford, V., & Diedrich, L. (2014). On "the evidence of experience" and its reverberations: An interview with Joan Scott. *Feminist Theory, 15*(2), 197–207.

Holcombe, T., Strand, E., Nugent, W., & Ng, Z. (2016). Veterinary social work: Practice within veterinary settings. *Journal of Human Behavior in the Social Environment, 26*(1), 69–80.

Holden, C. (2020). Characteristics of veterinary students: Perfectionism, personality factors, and resilience. *Journal of Veterinary Medical Education, 47*(4), 488–496.

Holley, K. (2009). Animal research practices and doctoral student identity development in a scientific community. *Studies in Higher Education, 34*(5), 577–591.

Howell, L., & Allen, S. (2019). Significant life experiences, motivations and values of climate change educators. *Environmental Education Research, 25*(6), 813–831.

Hulsbergen, M., Dop, P., Vernooij, J., & Burt, S. (2019). Teaching slaughter: Mapping changes in emotions in veterinary students during training in humane slaughter. *Journal of Veterinary Medical Education, 46*(1), 128–136.

Intergovernmental Panel on Climate Change. (2021). *Climate change 2021: The physical science basis. Summary for policymakers.* New York: United Nations. Retrieved from www.un.org/en/climatechange/reports

Irvine, L. (2008). Animals and sociology. *Sociology Compass, 2*(6), 1954–1971.

Irvine, L. (Ed.). (2019). *We are best friends: Animals in society.* Basel: MPDI Press.

Irvine, L., & Cilia, L. (2017). More-than-human families: Pets, people and practices in multi species households. *Sociology Compass, 11,* e12455. https://doi.org/10.1111/soc4.12455

Irvine, L., & Vermilya, J. (2010). Gender work in a feminized profession: The case of veterinary medicine. *Gender and Society, 24*(1), 56–82.

Izmirli, S., Yigit, A., & Phillips, C. J. C. (2014). Attitudes of Australian and Turkish students of veterinary medicine toward nonhuman animals and their careers. *Society & Animals, 22*(6), 580–601.

Jalongo, M. R. (Ed.). (2014). *Teaching compassion: Humane education in early childhood.* New York: Springer.

Jenkins, S., & Walter, D. (2016). *Esther the wonder pig: Changing the world one heart at a time.* New York: Grand Central Publishing.

Johnstone, E. C. S., Frye, M. A., Lord, L. K., Baysinger, A. K., & Edwards-Callaway, L. N. (2019). Knowledge and opinions of third year veterinary students relevant to animal welfare before and after implementation of a core welfare course. *Frontiers in Veterinary Science, 6*(103), 1–11.

Jones, S. (2003). *Valuing animals: Veterinarians and their patients in modern America.* Baltimore, MD: The John Hopkins University Press.

Jones, R. (2013). Science, sentience, and animal welfare. *Biology & Philosophy, 28*(1), 1–30.

Karaffa, K., & Hancock, T. (2019). Mental health experiences and service use among veterinary medical students. *Journal of Veterinary Medical Education, 46*(4), 449–458.

Karaffa, K., & Hancock, T. (2019a). Mental health stigma and veterinary medical students' attitudes toward seeking professional psychological help. *Journal of Veterinary Medical Education, 46*(4), 459–469.

Khan, A. (2019, June 27). U of G's OAC admits poster image was poor choice following online backlash. *Guleph Today.* Retrieved from www.gulephtoday.com

King, B. (2013). *How animals grieve.* Chicago: University of Chicago Press.

King, B. (2017). *Personalities on the plate: The lives and minds of animals we eat.* Chicago: University of Chicago Press.

Kirk, R., Pemberton, N., & Quick, T. (2019). Being well together? Promoting health and well being through more than human collaboration and companionship. *Medical Humanities, 45*(1), 75–81.

Klass, P. (1987/2010). *A not entirely benign procedure: Four years as a medical student.* New York: Kaplan Publishing.

Knesl, O., Hart, B., Fine, A., & Cooper, L. (2016). Opportunities for incorporating the human-animal bond in companion animal practice. *Journal of the American Veterinary Medical Association, 249*(1), 42–44.

Knopes, J. (2019). Science, technology, and human health: The value of STS in medical and health humanities pedagogy. *Journal of Medical Humanities, 40*, 461–471.

Knorr-Cetina, K. (1999). *Epistemic cultures: How the sciences make knowledge.* Cambridge, MA: Harvard University Press.

Kofman, A. (2018, October 25). Bruno Latour, the post-truth philosopher, mounts a defense of science. *New York Times.* Retrieved from www.nytimes.com

Kramer, C., McCaw, K., Zarestky, J., & Duncan, C. (2020). Veterinarians in a changing global climate: Educational disconnect and a path forward. *Frontiers in Veterinary Science, 7*, 613620. https://doi.org/10.3389/vets2020.613620

Kuhl, G. (2011). Representing animal-others in educational research. *Canadian Journal of Environmental Education, 16*, 106–121.

Kuhn, T. (1962). *The structure of scientific revolutions.* Chicago: University of Chicago Press.

Latour, B. (1987). *Science in action: How to follow scientists and engineers through society.* Cambridge, MA: Harvard University Press.

Latour, B. (2018). *Down to earth: Politics in the new climatic regime* (Porter, C., Trans.). Cambridge: Polity Press.

Latour, B., & Woolgar, S. (1979). *Laboratory life: The social construction of scientific facts.* Beverly Hills, CA: Sage Publications.

Laurent-Simpson, A. (2021). *Just like family: How companion animals joined the household.* New York: NYU Press.

Lave, J., & Wenger, E. (1991). *Situating learning: Legitimate peripheral participation.* Cambridge: Cambridge University Press.

Lawrence, E. (1994). Love for animals and the veterinary profession. *Journal of the American Veterinary Medical Association, 205*(7), 970–972.

Lawrence-Lightfoot, S. (2005). Reflection on portraiture: A dialogue between art and science. *Qualitative Inquiry, 11*(1), 3–15.

Lawrence-Lightfoot, S., & Davis, J. H. (1997). *The art and science of portraiture.* San Francisco, CA: Jossey-Bass.

Lecky, W. E. H. (1869). *History of European morals from Augustus to Charlemagne* (Vol. 1). London: Longmans, Green, and Company.

Lincoln, A. (2010). The shifting supply of men and women to occupations: Feminization in veterinary education. *Social Forces, 88*(5), 1969–1998.

Lindgren, N., & Öhman, J. (2019). A posthuman approach to human-animal relationships: Advocating critical pluralism. *Environmental Education Research, 25*(8), 1200–1215.

Linzey, A., & Linzey, C. (Eds.). (2017). *Animal ethics for veterinarians.* Urbana, IL: University of Illinois Press.

Littlewood, K., Beausoleil, N., Stafford, K., Stephens, C., Collins, T., Fawcett, A., . . . & Zito, S. (2020). How management of grief associated with ending the life of an animal is taught to Australasian veterinary students. *Australian Veterinary Journal, 98*(8), 356–363.

Liu, A., & van Gelderen, I. (2020). A systematic review of mental health—improving interventions in veterinary students. *Journal of Veterinary Medical Education, 47*(6), 745–758.

Lloro-Bidart, T. (2018). A feminist posthumanist multispecies ethnography for educational studies. *Educational Studies, 54*(3), 253–270.

Lloro-Bidart, T., & Banschbach, V. (Eds.). (2019). *Animals in environmental education: Interdisciplinary approaches to curriculum and pedagogy.* Cham, Switzerland: Palgrave-Macmillan.

Lloyd, J., & King, L. (2004). What are the veterinary schools and colleges doing to improve the nontechnical skills, knowledge, aptitudes, and attitudes of veterinary students? *Journal of the American Veterinary Medical Association, 224*(12), 1923–1924.

Lord, L., Millman, S., Carbone, L., Cook, N., Fisher, A., McKeegan, D., . . . & Patterson-Kane, E. (2017). A model curriculum for the study of animal welfare in colleges and schools of veterinary medicine. *Journal of the American Veterinary Medical Association, 250*(6), 632–640.

Lord, L., & Walker, J. (2009). An approach to teaching animal welfare issues at the Ohio State University. *Journal of Veterinary Medical Education, 36*(3), 276–279.

Lord, L., Walker, J., Croney, C., & Golab, G. (2010). A comparison of veterinary students enrolled and not enrolled in an Animal-Welfare course. *Journal of Veterinary Medical Education, 37*(1), 40–48.

Lowe, C. (2001). The trouble with tribe. *Teaching Tolerance* (spring). Retrieved from www.learningforjustice.org/magazine/spring-2001/the-trouble-with-tribe

Lupinacci, J. (2019). Teaching to end human supremacy <=> Learning to recognize equity in all species. In C. Drew et al. (Eds.), *Education for total liberation: Critical animal pedagogy and teaching against speciesism* (pp. 81–98). New York, NY: Peter Lang.

MacPete, R. (2018). *Lisette the vet.* San Diego, CA: Forest Lane Books.

Manette, C. (2004). A reflection on the way veterinarians cope with the death, euthanasia, and slaughter of animals. *Journal of the American Veterinary Medical Association, 225*(1), 34–38.

Martinsen, S., & Jukes, N. (2005). Towards a humane veterinary education. *Journal of Veterinary Medical Education, 32*(4), 454–460.

Martusewicz, R., Edmundson, J., & Lupinacci, J. (2015). *Ecojustice education: Toward diverse, democratic, and sustainable communities* (2nd ed.). New York, NY: Routledge.

McArthur, J. (2017). *We animals*. Brooklyn, NY: Lantern Books.

McCance, D. (2013). *Critical animal studies: An introduction*. Albany, NY: SUNY Press.

Mccomas, S. (1997). 15 myths: Lessons of misconceptions and misunderstandings from a science educator. *Skeptic, 5*(2), 88–96.

McInerney, J. (1993). Animals in education: Are we prisoners of false sentiment? *The American Biology Teacher, 55*(5), 276–280.

Melson, G. F. (2001). *Why the wild things are: Animals in the lives of children*. Cambridge, MA: Harvard University Press.

Menor-Campos, D. J., Diverio, S., Sánchez-Muñoz, C., López-Rodríguez, R., Gazzano, A., Palandri, L., & Mariti, C. (2019). Attitudes toward animals of students at three European veterinary medicine schools in Italy and Spain. *Anthrozoös, 32*(3), 375–385.

Menor-Campos, D. J., Knight, S., Sánchez-Muñoz, C., & López-Rodríguez, R. (2019). Human-directed empathy and attitudes toward animals use: A survey of Spanish veterinary students. *Anthrozoö, 32*(4), 471–487.

Midgley, M. (1979/1995). *Beast and man* (rev ed.). New York: Routledge.

Miner, H. (1956). Body rituals of the Nacirema. *American Anthropologist, 58*(3), 503–507.

Mitsuda, T. (2017). Entangled histories: German veterinary medicine, c. 1770–1900. *Medical History, 61*(1), 25–47.

Montgomery, S. (2018). *How to be a good creature: A memoir in thirteen animals*. Boston, MA: Houghton Mifflin Harcourt.

Morris, P. (2012). *Blue juice: Euthanasia in veterinary medicine*. Philadelphia, PA: Temple University Press.

Mossop, L. H., & Cobb, K. (2013). Teaching and assessing veterinary professionalism. *Journal of Veterinary Medical Education, 40*(3), 223–232.

Myers, Jr., G. (2013). Children, animals, and social neuroscience: Empathy, conservation education, and activism. In M. Bekoff (Ed.), *Ignoring nature no more: The case for compassionate conservation* (pp. 271–285). Chicago, IL: University of Chicago Press.

National Science Teachers Association. (2008). *NSTA position statement. Responsible use of live animals and dissection in the science classroom*. Arlington, VA: Author.

Newton, B., Barber, L., Clardy, J., Cleveland, E., & O'Sullivan, P. (2008). Is there hardening of the heart during medical school? *Academic Medicine, 83*(3), 244–249.

Nir, S. M., & Schweber, N. (2017, May 21). *After 146 years, Ringling Bros Circus takes its final bow*. Retrieved from www.nytimes.com

Nolen, R. (2011). Veterinarian's oath revised to emphasize animal welfare commitment. *JAVMA News*. Retrieved from www.avma.org/News/JAVMANews/Pages/x110101a.aspx

Oakley, J. (2009). Under the knife: Animal dissection as a contested school science activity. *Journal for Activist Science and Technology Education, 1*(2), 59–67.

Oakley, J. (2012). Science teachers and the dissection debate: Perspectives on animal dissection and alternatives. *International Journal of Environmental & Science Education, 7*(2), 253–267.

O'Brien, W., & Bates, P. (2015). "Looking and feeling the part": Developing aviation students' professional identity through a community of practice. *Teaching in Higher Education, 20*(8), 821–832.

One Health Commission. (2020). *What is one health?* Retrieved from www.onehealth commission.org/

Parson, G., Kinsman, S., Bosk, C., Sankar, P., & Ubel, P. (2001). Between two worlds: Medical student perceptions of humor and slang in the hospital setting. *Journal of General Internal Medicine, 16*, 544–549.

Payne, P. (1999). The significance of experience in SLE research. *Environmental Education Research, 5*, 365–381.

Peden, R., Camerlink, I., Boyle, L., Loughnan, S., Akaichi, F., & Turner, S. (2020). Belief in pigs' capacity to suffer: An assessment of pig farmers, veterinarians, students, and citizens. *Anthrozoös, 33*(1), 21–36.

Pedersen, H. (2004). Schools, speciesism, and hidden curricula: The role of critical pedagogy for human education futures. *Journal of Futures Studies, 8*(4), 1–14.

Pedersen, H. (2010). *Animals in schools: Processes and strategies in human-animal education.* West Lafayette, IN: Purdue University Press.

Pedersen, H. (2010a). Is "the posthuman" educable? On the convergence of educational philosophy, animal studies, and posthumanist theory. *Discourse: Studies in the Cultural Politics of Education, 31*(2), 237–250.

Pedersen, H. (2011). Animals and education research: Enclosures and openings. In P. Segerdahl (Ed.), *Undisciplined animals: Invitations to animal studies* (pp. 11–26). Cambridge: Cambridge Scholars Publishing.

Pedersen, H. (2013). Follow the Judas sheep: Materializing post-qualitative methodology in zooethnographic space. *International Journal of Qualitative Studies in Education, 26*(6), 717–731.

Pelias, R. (2015). A story located in "shoulds": Toward a productive future for qualitative inquiry. *Qualitative Inquiry, 21*(7), 609–611.

People for the Ethical Treatment of Animals. (2014). *Say "no" to classroom pets.* Retrieved from https//secure.peta.org

Pierce, J. (2016). *Run spot run: The ethics of keeping pets.* Chicago, IL: University of Chicago Press.

Pierce, J., & Bekoff, M. (2018). A postzoo future: Why welfare fails animals in zoos. *Journal of Applied Animal Welfare Science, 21*, 43–48.

Popkewitz, T. S. (1998). Dewey, Vygotsky, and the social administration of the individual: Constructivist pedagogy as systems of ideas in historical spaces. *American Educational Research Journal, 35*(4), 535–570.

Public Broadcasting System. (2012). *Nature. Animal odd couples: Studying the emotional lives of animals.* Available from www.pbs.org/wnet/nature/animal-odd-couples-video studying-the emotional-lives-of-animals/8028/

Rauktis, M., & Hoy-Gerlach, J. (2020). Animal (non-human) companionship for adults aging in place during COVID-19: A critical support, a source of concern and potential for social work responses. *Journal of Gerontological Social Work, 63*(6–7), 702–705.

Reese, J. (2018). *The end of animal farming: How scientists, entrepreneurs and activists are building an animal-free food system.* Boston, MA: Beacon Press.

Rice, S., & Rud, A. G. (Eds.). (2016). *The educational significance of non-human animal and animal interactions: Blurring the species line.* New York: Palgrave Macmillan.

Rice, S., & Rud, A. G. (Eds.). (2018). *Educational dimensions of school lunch: Critical perspectives.* New York: Palgrave Macmillan.

Richards, L., Coghlan, S., & Delany, C. (2020). "I had no idea that other people in the world thought differently to me": Ethical challenges in small animal veterinary practice and implications for ethics support and education. *Journal of Veterinary Medical Education, 47*(6), 728–738.

Risley-Curtiss, C., Rogge, M., & Kawam, E. (2013). Factors affecting social workers' inclusion of animals in practice. *Social Work, 58*(2), 153–161.

Rodriguez, K., Greer, J., Yatcilla, J., Beck, A., & O'Haire, M. (2020). The effects of assistance dogs on psychosocial health and wellbeing: A systematic literature review. *PLOS ONE, 15*(12), e0243302. https://doi.org/10.1371/journal.pone.0243302

Roff, S. (2015). Reconsidering the "decline" of medical student empathy as reported in studies using the Jefferson Scale of Physician Empathy-Student version (JSPE-S). *Medical
Teacher, 37*(8), 783–786.

Rollin, B. (2002, April 15). The use and abuse of Aesculapian authority in veterinary medicine. *Journal of the American Veterinary Medical Association, 220*(8), 1144–1149.

Rollin, B. (2019). Progress and absurdity in animal ethics. *Journal of Agricultural and
Environmental Ethics, 32*, 391–400.

Romo, V. (2019, April 2). *USDA terminates deadly cat experiments, plans to adopt out
remaining animals.* Retrieved from www.npr.org

Roth, W. M., & Lee, Y. J. (2007). "Vygotsky's neglected legacy": Cultural-historical activity
theory. *Review of Educational Research, 77*(2), 186–232.

Rud, A. G., & Beck, A. (2003). Companion animals in Indiana elementary schools.
Anthrozoös, 16(3), 241–251.

Rule, A., & Zhbanova, K. (2012). Changing perceptions of unpopular animals through facts,
poetry, crafts, and puppet plays. *Early Childhood Education Journal, 40*, 223–230.

Ryder, R. (1970). *Speciesism.* Oxford: Privately Printed Leaflet.

Safina, C. (2018). Where are zoos going-or are they gone? *Journal of Applied Animal Welfare
Science, 21*, 4–11.

Saldaña, J. (2003). *Longitudinal qualitative research: Analyzing change through time.*
Walnut Creek, CA: Altamira Press.

Schoenfeld-Tacher, R. M., Royal, K. D., & Flammer, K. (2016). Differences among veterinary students' and faculty members' perceptions of appropriate interactions with corporate entities at one US college of veterinary medicine. *Medical Science Education, 26*,
35–38.

Scholz, E., Trede, F., & Raidal, S. L. (2013). Workplace learning in veterinary education: A sociocultural perspective. *Journal of Veterinary Medical Education, 40*(4),
355–362.

Scott, J. (1991). The evidence of experience. *Critical Inquiry, 17*(4), 773–797.

Scully, M. (2002). *Dominion: The power of man, the suffering of animals, and the call to
mercy.* New York: St. Martin's Griffin.

Shapiro, K. (2018). Whither zoos? An inescapable question. *Journal of Applied Animal
Welfare Science, 21*, 1–3.

Shivley, C., Garry, F., Kogan, L., & Grandin, T. (2016). Survey of animal welfare, animal
behavior, and animal ethics courses in the curricula of AVMA Council of Education-
accredited veterinary colleges and schools. *Journal of the American Veterinary Medical
Association, 248*(10), 1165–1170.

Siegford, J. M., Cottee, S. Y., & Widowski, T. M. (2010). Opportunities for learning about
animal welfare from online courses to graduate degrees. *Journal of Veterinary Medical
Education, 37*(1), 49–55.

Singer, P. (1975). *Animal liberation.* New York: HarperCollins.

Singer, P. (1997). *The drowning child and the expanding circle.* Retrieved from www.newint.
org/features/1997/04/05/drowning

Skipper, A., & Gray, C. (2021). Launch of the veterinary humanities network. *VetRecord,
188*(6), 233.

Snaza, N., & Weaver, J. (Eds.). (2015). *Posthumanism and educational research.* Abingdon,
UK: Routledge.

Solot, D., & Arluke, A. (1997). Learning the scientist's role: Animal dissection in middle
school. *Journal of Contemporary Ethnography, 26*(1), 28–54.

Spannring, R. (2017). Animals in environmental education research. *Environmental
Education Research, 23*(1), 63–74.

Sufian, S., Blackie, M., Michel, J., & Garden, R. (2020). Centering patients, revealing structures: The Health Humanities Portrait Approach. *Journal of Medical Humanities, 21*, 459–479.

Sullivan, W. M., Colby, A., Wegner, J. W., Bond, L., & Schulman, L. S. (2007). *Educating lawyers: Preparation for the profession of law.* San Francisco, CA: John Wiley & Sons.

Sunstein, C., & Nussbaum, M. (Eds.). (2004). *Animal rights: Current debates and new directions.* Oxford: Oxford University Press.

Tannenbaum, J. (1993). Veterinary medical ethics: A focus of conflicting interests. *Journal of Social Issues, 49*(1), 143–156.

Tanner, T. (1980). Significant life experiences: A new research area in environmental education. *The Journal of Environmental Education, 11*(4), 20–24.

Taylor, A. (2017). Beyond stewardship: Common world pedagogies for the anthropocene. *Environmental Education Research, 23*(10), 1448–1461.

Taylor, A., & Pacini-Ketchabaw, V. (2019). *The common worlds of children and animals: Relational ethics for entangled lives.* New York: Routledge.

Teng, V., Nguyen, C., Hall, K., Rydel, T., Sattler, A., Schillinger, E., . . . & Lin, S. (2017). Rethinking empathy decline: Results from an OSCE. *The Clinical Teacher, 14*, 441–445.

Timmerman, N., & Ostertag, J. (2011). Too many monkeys jumping on their heads: Animal lessons within young children's media. *Canadian Journal of Environmental Education, 16*, 59–75.

Tomasi, S., Fechter-Leggett, E., Edwards, N., Reddish, A., Crosby, A., & Nett, R. (2019). Suicide among veterinarians in the United States from 1979 through 2015. *Journal of the American Veterinary Medical Association, 254*(1), 104–112.

Toulmin, S. (1982). The construal of reality: Criticism in modern and postmodern science. *Critical Inquiry, 9*(1), 93–111.

Turner, V. (1969). *The ritual process: Structure and anti-structure.* Chicago, IL: Aldine.

Van Gennep, A. (1908/1960). *The rites of passage* (Vizedom, M. B., & Caffee, G. L., Trans.). London: Routledge and Kegan Paul.

Vermilya, J. (2012). Contesting horses: Borders and shifting social meanings in veterinary medical education. *Society & Animals, 20*(2), 123–137.

Vermilya, J. (2015). *Tracking "large" or "small": Boundaries and their consequences for veterinary students within the tracking system.* Unpublished PhD. Dissertation, University of Colorado.

Vinson, A. (2018). Short white coats: Knowledge, identity, and status negotiations of first-year medical students. *Symbolic Interaction, 42*(3), 395–411.

Wadman, M. (2019, April 9). *Scientists decry USDA's decision to end cat parasite research.* Retrieved from www.sciencemag.org/

Waldau, P. (2007). Veterinary education as leader: Which alternatives? *Journal of Veterinary Medical Education, 34*(5), 605–614.

Ward, E., Oven, A., & Bethencourt, R. (2020). *The clean pet food revolution: How better pet food will change the world.* Brooklyn, NY: Lantern Publishing and Media.

Ware, C. (2017). Personal experience narratives in veterinary medicine. *Narrative Culture, 4*(2), 201–221.

Ware, C. (2018). Veterinary medicine and the spiritual imagination: A body-centered approach. *Journal of Folklore Research, 55*(2), 9–36.

Warren, A. L., & Donnon, T. (2013). Optimizing biomedical science learning in a veterinary curriculum: A review. *Journal of Veterinary Medical Education, 40*(3), 210–222.

Weis, L., Kupper, M. M., Ciupak, Y., Stich, A., Jenkins, H., & Lalonde, C. (2011). Sociology of education in the United States, 1966–2008. In S. Tozer, B. Gallegos, A. Henry, M. B. Greiner, & P. G. Price (Eds.), *Handbook of research in the social foundations of education* (pp. 15–40). New York: Routledge.

Wilkie, R. (2010). *Livestock/deadstock: Working with farm animals from birth to slaughter.* Philadelphia, PA: Temple University Press.

Willis, P. (1977). *Learning to labor: How working-class kids get working-class jobs.* New York: Columbia University Press.

Wilson, E. O. (1984). *Biophilia.* Cambridge, MA: Harvard University Press.

Wise, S. (2000). *Rattling the cage: Towards legal rights for animals.* Cambridge, MA: Da Capo Press.

Woods, A. (2017). From one medicine to two: The evolving relationship between human and veterinary medicine in England, 1791–1835. *Bulletin of the History of Medicine, 91*(3), 494–523.

Zasloff, R. L., Hart, L., & DeArmond, H. (1999). Animals in elementary school education in California. *Journal of Applied Animal Welfare Science, 2*(4), 347–357.

Index

Note: Page numbers followed by "n" indicate a note on the corresponding page.

4-H (head, heart, hand, and health), 12n3

A

AAVMC, *see* American Association of
    Veterinary Medical Colleges
adjusting to uncertainty, 88–89
African National Congress, 127
aggression, 109
American Association of Veterinary Medical
    Colleges, 6, 12n7, 18, 23n5, 40
American Holistic Veterinary Medicine
    Association, 122
American Pet Product Association, 3
American Veterinary Medical Association, 3, 18,
    20, 32, 92
animal abuse, 64, 67–68, 135
Animal Advocates of Greater Lafayette, 137
animal appearance
    as sites of sentimentality, 13–15
    as teaching and learning tools, 15
    as trope and antithesis of humanity, 17–18
animal behavior, 9, 15, 48
animal centric anthropomorphism, 110
animal cognition and emotion, 108
animal dissection, 39, 47–48
    centrality of, 15
    dead dogs, 46–48
    emotional distancing strategies for, 16
    experiencing, 16
    horse, 47
animal health, 4, 7, 19–20, 71, 92, 94, 116
animal learning, 9
animal memories, 10, 30, 31–32
"animal mentation," 108
animal pronouns, calling for change in, 120
animal rights, 4, 7, 27, 30, 45, 116, 120
    organizations, 132
    and "teaching dogs," link between, 45–46
animal shelters, 1, 4, 7, 35, 39, 59, 72, 130–131
animals raised for food, *see* "food" animals
animals raised for slaughter, 19, 37, 41, 52–53,
    67–68, 95, 116–117, 126
    and handlers, relationship between, 53
    learning about separation from, 34–38
    medical care demand for, 19
animal suffering, 19–20, 22, 36, 40, 56, 67, 69,
    70–72, 80, 92–95, 100, 104, 115–119,
    122, 136

animal welfare, 4–5, 7, 20, 27, 30, 67–68, 92,
    94–95, 104, 116, 120, 132
anthropocentric anthropomorphism, 110
anthropology, 5, 108
anthropomorphism, 17, 109–110
anxiety in veterinary school, 81–82, 85, 89, 100, 136
apartheid, 127–129
Associated Press, joint open letter to, 120
Association of Professional Humane Educators, 1
attachment to animals, *see* connections to animals
attitudes toward animal welfare, 2, 16, 21, 29, 55,
    57, 131–132
aviation students, 65
AVMA, *see* American Veterinary Medical
    Association

B

BAI, *see* Bureau of Animal Industry
behaviorist mindset, 23n3
biophilia thesis, 14
borders and boundaries, 138n2
Brazilian Amazon, destruction in, 121
Bureau of Animal Industry, 19, 20

C

CAFOs, *see* confined animal feeding operations
campus-based rotations, experiences of
    cultural issues, 84
    disappointment, 83
    emotional burnout, 88–89
    exploited as free labor, 81–82
    in large animal hospital, 82–83
    reasons for sharing, 85
    resenting nurses' authority, 83
    in small animal hospital, 81–82
    working with clients, 85
Cartesian dualism, 101–102, 107
cats, 1, 3, 15–16, 19–20, 35, 63, 65, 71–72, 119,
    129–130
    Paw Project, 131
    research, 77n3
    writing descriptions of, 130
Central Midwest University, 8, 25–26, 30, 39, 41,
    43–45, 51, 53, 56, 61–64, 73, 89, 92, 118
    administrative offices, 59
    dog cadavers at, 47–48
    on vacation and professional experience, 63

Cerenia, 119–120
chicken lab, 43
   chickens, 4, 8, 10, 19, 40–41, 53–58, 81, 95, 126
   experiences of, 53–56
   focus on technique, 53
classroom pets, 15
classroom zoo trips, 14–15
clay paw imprint, 97n1
"clean" pet food, 119
climate change, acceleration of, 121
clinical rotations, 10–11, 26, 59–64, 60, 67, 70,
     72, 74, 79, 82–86, 89, 92–93, 96,
     105–106, 133–135
CMU, *see* Central Midwest University
cognitive ethology, 9, 11, 28, 100, 108, 109,
     130–131
   and anthropomorphism, 109–110
   behavioral patterns of animals, 107–108
   magpie behavior, 108–109
community practice sites, 59
companion animals, 2–4, 8, 20, 26, 33, 41,
     68–69, 118, 120
   health of, 19–20
   shelters, 72
companion track option, 42
compassion, 37, 51–52, 64, 117, 130
confined animal feeding operations, 8
conflicts, 21–22, 43, 46, 52, 80, 85, 94–95, 126
"connection/disconnection," framework of, 31
connections to animals, 14, 30, 37, 45, 62, 67,
     69, 73, 75–76, 81, 88, 91, 94, 102,
     110, 113, 115, 122, 130–131, *see also*
     emotional connections
   dogs, 31
   for emotional support, 31–32, 34
   limits and barriers for, 34–35
   maintaining and strengthening, 105–107
   by naming, 36
coping with pressure, approaches to, 87
   adjusting to uncertainty, 88–89, 105
   emotional "energy" with animals, 90
   renewal of commitment, 91, 106
   resistance, 89–90, 106
   shift in language, 90–91
COVID-19 pandemic, 6, 113, 121

D

"Day in the Life" assignment, 138n4
dead animals, 16, 39, 46–48, 116–117
Descartes' Error (Damasio), 107
Descartes, R, 44, 101, 107–108, 120
desegregated schools, research studies on, 129
disconnection from animals, 31, 52, 79, 81, 86,
     110, 113, 115
   among high school and college students, 35

   challenges of, 34
   creating experiences for, 37–38
   volunteer experiences for, 35
Doctorate of Veterinary Medicine, 18, 96, 126
dog cadavers, at CMU, 47–48
dogs, 1, 3, 6, 8, 10, 31–32, 34, 40, 51–52, 63, 71,
     73, 91, 108, 117, 119
   and cats, 19–20
   classified as "small animal," 44
   dead, dissection of, 46–48
   dog labs, 39–40, 46
   importance in veterinary education,
     44–45
dualism of heart and mind, 101
DVM, *see* Doctorate of Veterinary Medicine

E

education
   humane, 1–2, 11
   multicultural, 27, 130–131
Emergency Critical Care rotation, 80
emotional attachment, 44, 86, 117
emotional connections, 11, 68, 72, 90, *see also*
     connections to animals
emotional detachment, 16, 64–65
emotional "energy" with animals, 90
emotions for animals, 11, 16, 32, 34–35, 39–41,
     52, 62–67, 69, 79, 82, 84, 101–102,
     105, 107–108, 115–117
   during early months of clinical year, 67
   euthanasia process and, 55–56
   impact on students' progress, 116
   in large animal hospital, 67–71
   and reason, fundamental dichotomy
     between, 101
   in small animal hospital, 71–72
   of witnessing bovine slaughter, 116–117
   of witnessing pig slaughterhouse, 117
empathy, 27, 31, 44, 46, 52, 64, 85, 108, 110,
     130–131, 133
employment plan, 79
Equine Community Practice, 63
"Esther the Wonder Pig," 77n4, 117
ethical concerns, negotiating
   in large animal hospital, 67–71
   in small animal hospital, 71–72
ethical issues around animals, 8, 17, 21–22, 53,
     55–56, 119, 132, 135–136
ethnographic study, of South African school,
     127–129
Eurocentric science, 101
euthanasia, 36, 48, 53–55, 68–70, 69, 72, 80,
     86–87, 90–91, 93, 104, 116
explicit learning about animals, 2–3
externships, 80

F

farm animals, 34, 52–53, 117
federal oversight and regulation, 19
feelings and emotions of students, 115
fleeting moments, 79–80
"Flint's Story: Education and Justice for
   Animals" (essay), 130
"food" animals, 34–38, 41, 57, 68, 100, 120, 126
formal curriculum, 43
formal schooling, 1–2
free labor for veterinary hospital, exploitation
   as, 81–82
FreeSA, *see* Fund for a Free South Africa
fresh cadavers, 47–48
frustration of medical student, 104
Fund for a Free South Africa, 127

G

"good" veterinarian, epitome of being, 101
graduation, 7, 18, 29, 59–61, 79, 81, 85, 96, 116

H

handlers and animals raised for slaughter,
   relationship between, 53
"Happily Ever Esther Farm Sanctuary," 117
"hardening of heart" model, 31
Health Humanities Portrait, 112–113
"herd consensus," 17–18
high school fetal pig dissection lab, 16
Hippocratic Oath, 62
horses, 3, 8, 18, 20, 26, 32, 34, 36, 41, 69–71, 86,
   106, 118
   dissection of, 47
   positioned in "companion" and "large" track,
      41, 42
   replacement with automobiles, 19, 24n8
human–animal bond, 4, 20, 30, 32–33, 53, 101,
   107, 113
   articles on, 101
   in context of farm animals, 53
   definition of, 32
   social and cultural context of, 33, 37
human–animal relationships, 2, 5, 10, 102, 133
human animals, 1, 3, 9, 110, 122, 133
human clients, interactions with, 6, 21, 62,
   68–69, 71, 72, 80, 82, 101, 112,
   119–120
   after sleepless days, 104–105
   challenges of handling, 85, 87
   effective communication, 86–87
   empathizing with clients, 85–86
   fourth-year students as primary contact for,
      72–73, 85

   owner's relationship with animal, 86
   personal connection, 73–74
   sense of "energy" as way for, 90
   U.S. clients, 87
human-created cycles of time, 28
humane approach, 103
humane education graduate certificates, 2
humane education programs, 1
humane slaughter, course on, 116
humanism, 107, 112, 120
   Goldberg's insistence on centering, 120
   and professionalism, conflict between, 22–23,
      80–81, 104
humanist perspective to suffering, 103–104
human learning, 9
human owners, 41, 44, 62, 64, 68–69, 71–73,
   80, 86–88, 90, 92, 103, 106, 126,
   134–136, *see also* human clients,
   interactions with
human use value, treating animals depending
   on, 14

I

IACUC, *see* Institutional Animal Care and Use
   Committee
Institutional Animal Care and Use Committee,
   44, 131–132
Institutional Review Board, 85, 122, 132
interviews in research study, 60–61, 76–77n2,
   133–135

J

Journal of Veterinary Medical Education, The
   (JVME), 6
junior doctors, 75

K

"kitten cannibalism" project, 77n3

L

"laboratory life," 103
Laboratory Life (Latour and Woolgar), 125
land clearing for cattle production, 121
large animal hospital, 40–41, 67–71, 82–84, 86,
   106, 118, 126
learning, banking approach to, 8
licensed veterinarians, 80
liminality, concept of, 61
live dogs, 44, 47
livestock auctions, 66
lockstep "scientific method," myth of, 101
longitudinal qualitative research, 27–28

love for animals, 99, 100, 101, 107
  adjusting to uncertainty, 105
  "science" and, 102–104

M

magpie funeral, 108–109
Mandela, Nelson, 127
mass media, 120
"mechanic" model of veterinary education, 68, 95–96
medical education, 21–22, 28, 63, 80, 112, 126, 132
  research on, 5
  significant changes in, 39–40
medical humanities, 11, 110–113
medical schools, 18, 31, 40, 62, 65, 104
medical students, 22, 31, 47–48, 56, 63, 104–105, 111–112
  discomfort with dog lab, 40
  focus on clinical years of training, 39
  socialization to death, 39
  status of white coat for, 62
  transition to complete insiders, 104
  white coat ceremonies, 62
mental health issues, 100
  anxiety, 81–82, 85, 89, 100
  distress, 85, 134, 136
moral concern for animals, Descartes' arguments against, 107
moral judgements, 80
motivations for veterinary profession, 10, 18, 20, 29, 121
  to help people, 33–34
  uncomfortable with human blood, 36–37

N

narrative medicine, 113
National Research Act of 1974, 138n5
national veterinary board exams, preparation for, 60
NAVLE, *see* North American Veterinary Licensing Examination
non-human animals, 13, 75, 120
non-pet animals, 14
North American Veterinary Licensing Examination, 60, 79
nurses' authority, resenting, 83

O

objective science, 101
off-campus rotations, *see also* clinical rotations
  experiences of, 80, 83–84
  focus of, 59, 60

on-campus rotations, *see* clinical rotations
One Health, 3
Ontario Agricultural College, 118
Ontario Veterinary College, 117–118
outsider research, 126–127
OVC, *see* Ontario Veterinary College
oxygen, 121–122

P

Parallel Chart, 111, 113
Paw Project, 122, 131
pediatrician approach to veterinary profession, 68, 91
Pegaso scanner, 118
pet, *see also* cats; dogs; horses; pigs
  adoptions during COVID-19 pandemic, 23n6
  food, 119
  increase in numbers of, 3
  pigs, 106, 126
"pet effect," 33
pet food companies, 118–119
pig and chicken labs, segmented professional socialization in, 43
pig farms
  farm inspections of, 53
  real-world context of, 50–51
pig labs, 48, 50–55
  experiences of, 50–52
  pedagogical objective of, 52–53
  role in professional socialization, 50–51
pig roast on OVC's campus, public opposition to, 118
pigs, 4, 6, 10, 16, 19, 26, 33–34, 40–41, 43, 81, 86, 100, 106, 117, 126
  as "border" category, 41
  farm practices involving, 49–50
  status in large animal hospital, 106
pig snaring, 48, 49–50, 53, 57
portraiture, 112
positive feedback, 73
positivist science, 108
possum, intubating, 63
preschool education, 44
prioritization of duty, 80
privacy of participant, 28
professional fields, outsiders' research in, 126–127
professional identity, 10, 22, 29, 40, 43, 56, 67, 80, 81, 112
professionalism, 10, 81, 89, 103, 105, 107, 112, 120
  and humanism, conflict between, 22–23, 80–81, 104, 112
  in medical education field, 22
  and veterinary identity, 9, 21–23

professional socialization, 2, 10, 18, 39–40,
        42–43, 46, 49–50, 51, 55–57, 62
    intubation of possum, 63
    pig lab role in, 50–51
    practicing in real-world context, 63
    real-world practices as source of, 55
    white coat ceremonies, 62–63
public health initiatives, 19
Public Responsibility in Medicine and Research
        (PRIMR), 138n5
Purdue animal care, 44

Q

qualitative inquiry, 112
qualitative research, 27, 104, 127

R

race, ethnicity, and nationality, 28
Rainbow Bridge, 91
RAVS, *see* Rural Area Veterinary Services
reason and emotion, fundamental dichotomy
        between, 101
regulatory veterinarian, 94
relationship with animals, 31, 118, *see also*
        connections to animals
renewal of commitment, 81, 87–89, 91, 99, 105,
        106
researcher, classic dilemma of, 126
research project frameworks
    animal stories, 28
    of "connection/disconnection," 31
    human stories, 28
    longitudinal qualitative research, 27–28
    of "significant life experiences," 29–30
research study participants, *see also* animal
        memories; human-animal bond
    diversity of, 25–26
    interviews, 26–27
    tracks of specialization, 26
resistance, 89–90, 106
restraining dog, 49
Rural Area Veterinary Services, 63, 90

S

science, 102
    classroom, 15–16
    and new animal stories, 107–110
    positivist, 108
    as series of steps, 101
Science, Technology, and Society, 102
scientism, 101–103
scientists, 101–102
    stereotypes about, 107
    study of animal empathy, 109

segmented collective identity, 52, 95, 100
Shelter Animal Medicine program, 7
significant life experiences, 29–30, 61
    emotional detachment, 64–66
    intubation of possum, 63
    livestock auction, 66–67
    mobile veterinary clinic, 63–64
    practicing in real-world context, 63
    use of detached language, 64–65
single scientific method, notion of, 101
SLE, *see* significant life experiences
small animal, 20, 26, 34, 44, 47, 53
    hospital, 41, 71–72, 81–82, 105
    medicine, 20, 51, 82, 101
    mentality, 41, 42, 48, 69
    terminal surgeries, 47
    tracks, 40–41, 43, 100
socialization, 2, 10, 18, 39, 42–43
social justice, 125
social work field, 113
societal change in human-animal relationships,
        28
societal perspectives on animals, changing,
        3–4
South African high school, ethnography in,
        127–129
species divide, 120
speciesism, 133
species-linked behavior, generalizations of, 109
stress and exhaustion, 96
STS, *see* Science, Technology, and Society
suicide rates among veterinarians, 100
summer after second year of veterinary school,
        59
survey research, 7–8
swine medicine specialty, 51
swine snare, 49
sympathy cards, 73

T

teacher education program, 2
"teaching dogs", 44, 45–46
terminal labs, 47
third year of veterinary school, 10, 30, 59, 60–62,
        74
"through line," centrality of, 28
tiger park, conversation about, 134–135
time management, 61
tracks of specialization, CMU, 41
tracks of system, 26, 47, 50, 57, 64
    administrative mechanisms of, 40
    cracks and fissures in, 41–42
    "small" and "large" animal, 40–41
transitional liminality, 62, 74–75, 79, 96, 104,
        105
trust, 51, 56–57, 81, 87

U

"unfeeling scientist," idea of, 16
United Nations Intergovernmental Panel on
        Climate Change, 122
University of Arizona, 18
U.S. anti-apartheid movement, 127

V

VALE, *see* Vets Against Live Export
veterinarians, 2–4, 6, 18–21, 19, 29, 35, 37,
        39–41, 46–47, 51, 54, 56–57, 62,
        65–66, 72, 79–80, 86, 92–93,
        100–103, 105, 121–122
    average starting salary for, 18, 21
    as doctors for pets, 20
    ethical and moral challenges of being, 4
    fixation on one problem, 103
    as mechanics, 68
    as pediatricians, 68
    rise in demand for, 20
    as teachers, 8
veterinary care, spending on, 3
veterinary colleges, 4–5, 8–9, 18, 25, 40–41,
        43–45, 51, 57–60, 63, 79, 118
veterinary curriculum, 6, 10, 13–14, 19, 26,
        39–40, 45, 55, 59, 79, 89, 112, 115,
        136
    chicken lab, 53–56
    dead dogs, 47–48
    live dogs, 44–47
    need for change in, 4–5
    snaring swine, 48–53
    students' reactions to, 43
veterinary education, 5–12, 10, 18–23, 27–31,
        37, 40, 42, 44, 46–48, 61, 67, 69, 72,
        79–81, 85, 95–96, 99, 102, 105, 112,
        115, 117–119, 121–122, 132–133, 136
    cycle of, 29
    loans for, 18
    philosophical framework of, 8–9
    questions to ask of, 6
    research studies, 5–7
    role of, 3–5
veterinary humanities, 11, 100, 110–114, 126,
        133
veterinary identity and professionalism, 21–23
veterinary medicine, 2, 17, 20–21, 30, 33, 36–37,
        40–42, 44, 52, 56–59, 64, 67–69, 72,
        85, 87, 92, 95, 110, 112–119, 113, 115,
        129
    concern about outsider' critique, 126
    love and scientism in, 100–105
    nexus of multiple fields, 113
    signs of change in, 126–127

veterinary oath, 5, 7, 11, 62, 81, 107
    "animal welfare" inclusion in, 4, 20–21, 92
    established by AVMA, 20
    inherent conflicts in, 93–95
    meaning for students, 92–96
    "prevention of animal suffering" part of, 93–95
    "scientific knowledge and skills" part of,
        102–103
    words contained in, 92
veterinary profession, 2–4, 6–7, 9–11, 18–21, 29,
        33–34, 37, 41, 43–44, 46, 48, 51–52,
        56–57, 61–62, 64–65, 67, 71, 74,
        79–81, 85, 89–92, 95, 99–101, 103,
        105, 107, 120, 126–127, 132, *see also*
        love for animals
    challenges to change, 122
    changes following societal shifts, 4
    companion animal health side of, 19–20
    contradictions inherent in, 39
    decision to research, 127, 131
    devaluing of, 102
    "non-technical competence" within, 21
    role in human–animal relationships, 2
    scope of, 3
veterinary school representative
    for pet food company, 118–119
    for pet pharmaceutical corporation, 119
veterinary schools, 3, 6–7, 10, 21–22, 25–27,
        29–30, 37, 42–44, 47–48, 51, 54, 56,
        59–60, 62–63, 65, 75, 81, 85, 89–90,
        92, 96, 100, 118–120, 132
    admission requirements, 35, 41
    fall in enrollments to, 19
    licensure and state regulation, 18–19
    rise in number of applicants to, 18
veterinary social work, 113
Vets Against Live Export, 122
volunteer experience, 35

W

weekend jobs of animal care, 39
white coat ceremony, 92
    importance for medical students, 63
    importance for veterinary students, 62–63
    of medical school and veterinary school, 62
White Coat Waste Project, 77n3

Y

youth livestock program, qualitative study of, 1

Z

Zoetis, 20
zoos, 14–15

Printed in Great Britain
by Amazon

23077213R00099